SOLAR ENERGY

HANS RAU

TRANSLATED FROM THE GERMAN
BY MAXIM SCHUR.

TRANSLATION EDITED AND REVISED
BY D. J. DUFFIN.

The energy emitted by the sun is too important to be neglected; it pays us to utilize it. The gradual exhaustion of fossil fuels compels mankind to meet its requirements for power to an increasing extent with atomic and solar energy. Coal and oil, the basic material for many dyestuffs, pharmaceutical products, drugs, plastics, etc., are too precious to be used exclusively as fuels in power stations and households. Solar energy, on the other hand, has become an increasingly practical commodity. Recent experiments resulted in conversion of solar energy into conventional energy in the ratio of an even fourteen per cent.

The scope and depth of this work are the result of the author's attempts to investigate and summarize achievements in the field of solar energy from all over the world. The first portion, dealing with the physics of the sun, gives many valuable sidelights on its constitution and behavior. After an appreciation of the "pioneers of solar energy," numerous applications are explained: solar distillation units, solar cookers, solar melting furnaces, solar power engines, and solar power plants. The

(Continued on back flap)

SOLAR ENERGY

HANS RAU

TRANSLATED BY MAXIM SCHUR

Edited and Revised by

D. J. DUFFIN

THE MACMILLAN COMPANY, NEW YORK
COLLIER-MACMILLAN LIMITED, LONDON

EDITOR'S PREFACE

This American edition of Hans Rau's highly successful German book stems from an earlier English translation commissioned by Macmillan from Max Schur in 1959. Although Mr. Schur's translation was faithful in every respect to the original, the publisher and author both subsequently agreed that something approaching a new edition was needed for American readers—one that would include more examples of recent U.S. accomplishments in the field of solar energy and would also incorporate the author's own additions to the subject since 1958, when the work first appeared in West Germany under the imprint of Athenäum-Verlag, Bonn.

The present book, therefore, is an approved revision of the first translation, interspersed throughout with a rather free retranslation and amplification by the editor, yet based on the original German text and adhering to Mr. Rau's plan and scope as closely as possible. With the author's kind permission the editor has added some 30,000 words to the book in order to embrace developments since 1958 as well as to broaden its interest in accordance with the author's own intentions. Mr. Rau has read and approved the manuscript and has added a number of new illustrations and comments.

Both author and editor wish to acknowledge with deep appreciation the invaluable assistance of Professor Erich A. Farber of the University of Florida, who has made many constructive suggestions toward improving the new edition, and who has written a new final chapter summarizing present and anticipated research and development in solar energy.

D. J. DUFFIN

Yardley, Pa.
October, 1963

CONTENTS

1 ENERGY FOR THE FUTURE

Every invention or scientific discovery that is now an accepted part of our daily lives was at one time called "fantastic" or "impossible." Imagine what our eighteenth century forbears, if they could return to earth for a brief moment, would think about our present-day "fantasies" of radio, television, sports cars, jet planes, and electronic computers!

These and many other inventions are the products of human ingenuity. We have almost become the lords of nature—in our own estimation. But though we may acknowledge our dependence on the earth for coal, oil and other energy sources, we remain for the most part oblivious to the fact that the sun is actually the source of all our energy. When we burn wood, we release the solar energy that was stored in the living tree by chemical action. The fossil fuels—coal and oil, as well as natural gas—are, in effect, imprisoned solar energy; they are the remains of plant material that flourished millions of years ago in sunlight. Even the food we eat is the product of solar energy, transmuted into plant and animal tissue.

Besides the energy we obtain from fuels, our vast hydroelectric power network is also a product of solar energy. The sun's rays are the engine that keeps the water cycle going. The heat of the sun evaporates the water of the seas and lakes, causes the resulting water vapor to be carried aloft and form clouds, then condense into precipitation or falling water—to fill the brooks and rivers which in turn drive the huge water turbogenerators that generate electricity.

The radiation emitted by the sun into space amounts to about 378 billion billion (378,000,000,000,000,000,000) kilowatts—a fantastic figure indeed. Even the infinitesimal amount that reaches the earth—170 trillion kilowatts—is an incomprehensible figure. The entire capacity of the Tennessee Valley Authority (TVA) is about 12 million kilowatts; its Kingston plant, largest steam power plant in the world, has a capacity of about 1.5 million kw. Compare either of these figures with the kilowatt output of the solar power plant and the fraction of it that reaches the earth. We would have to build 170 million Kingston power plants to match the amount of solar energy received by the earth.

Solar energy costs nothing to generate, transmit or distribute. We can utilize it with inexpensive equipment in many practical ways—cooking food, heating or distilling water, heating homes, rectifying alcohol, obtaining salt and other minerals from the sea, operating air-conditioning plants, melting and processing of metals and ceramics at temperatures up to 7000° F, and as a substitute for electricity in a variety of industrial operations.

Utilization of solar energy is becoming more and more significant as we use up other sources of energy and are obliged to develop new fuels for the future. Those that have served up to now are fast diminishing.

The development of each new form of energy has required a good deal of time, money and experience, preceded by inevitable waste. Before the invention of the steam engine, nobody apparently thought of utilizing the steam generated in countless boilers and vats. Water power, or "white coal" of the French, went unused for centuries, perhaps millennia, before its enormous energy could be transformed into electric power. And although atoms were known to exist since about 1800, nobody talked seriously about harnessing atomic power until 1939.

Similarly, the harnessing of solar energy faces a period of development, trial and error until the proper formula for its economic utilization has been found. One thing is certain, however—the problem is considerably less complicated in the case of solar power lavished on us by nature than for any other form of energy. All we have to do is observe, study and learn how the immense forces that daily reach our earth can be most efficiently collected, stored and converted.

[2]

The solar radiation received by the Sahara alone would, according to an estimate by General Félix Pasteur, be sufficient to generate 1,000 times as much power as we would get if we burned all of our coal resources at once. In other words, if we cover only one-thousandth part of the Sahara with solar mirrors, we can theoretically obtain enough solar energy to eliminate the need for coal. We say "theoretically," because losses in the transmission and conversion of power would, at present, be considerable.

With proper utilization of solar energy, deserts such as the Sahara can be transformed into orchards, gardens and farmland with the help of large-scale projects, now in the planning stage, for removing the salt from sea water. Irrigation would do the rest.

2 POWER FOR FIVE BILLION PEOPLE

About 5,000 nuclear reactors of present-day "small" design (15,000–30,000 kw), using either pressurized-water or boiling-water principles, will be sufficient, according to Dr. George Brown of Michigan College of Mining and Technology, to provide 20 percent of the power requirements of the world in the next 50 years. (One may expect, however, that the design of nuclear reactors will become considerably more efficient in the next half century.) The largest nuclear power plant in operation anywhere in the world is the Dresden, Ill., plant of the Commonwealth Edison Company of Chicago, which began operating in June of 1960 with a total capacity of 180,000 kw. It is expected that by 1965 this record will be exactly doubled by the 360,000-kw nuclear power plant now being completed by Westinghouse for the Southern California Edison Company. Early in 1963, Consolidated Edison Company of New York announced plans for a 1,000,000-kw atomic power plant in New York City.

Nuclear power has its limitations, however, both as to cost and efficiency. Despite the indicated advances, mankind is confronted with the necessity of developing and exploiting still other sources of power. Without question, solar energy is such a source, even though we have let it go to waste since the dawn of human life. It's Dr. Brown's opinion that the utilization of solar energy is today more or less in the same stage of development as nuclear energy was in 1945 after the explosion of the first atomic bomb

[4]

at Alamogordo, New Mexico. Within a few decades, by expending the equivalent amount of scientific and technical effort on solar energy, it should not be difficult to meet the power requirements of the whole world with its greatly increased population.

What solar energy can mean to us is illustrated by the following example. If an area of approximately 6,500 square miles of desert land in New Mexico were covered with solar mirrors, enough power could be obtained—assuming only 10 percent efficiency of conversion—to satisfy the entire power requirements of the United States. The 6,500-square-mile area required for the solar mirrors is a mere 1/6,000 of the nation's land area. Small-scale collection experiments have already produced a conversion efficiency of 8 percent. But even if only 3 percent of the solar energy incident on one-tenth of the earth's land area were converted into usuable power it would be enough to meet the power requirements of a world population of 6 billion—twice the present population.

Naturally we will need more than a battery of solar mirrors to make this power available. Specially designed transmission lines and other technical equipment must be provided so that solar energy can be delivered thousands of miles from the source without appreciable losses. But there is no question that such problems will be solved with twentieth-century technology.

And the twenty-first century? Less than forty years distant, the new century may see a world populated by 5 billion people—a world, as Dr. Brown envisages, in which the standard of living will be far higher than today's, a world that no longer has to burn valuable chemical materials to provide power for its machines but instead has harnessed the energy of the nucleus and of the sun itself.

3 POWER RESERVES—TODAY AND TOMORROW

The average motorist doesn't give much thought to the problem of how much gasoline will be available for our descendants in A.D. 2000. Maybe new petroleum resources will have been discovered by then; maybe the twenty-first century motorist will simply plug into a nuclear power source every 200 or 5,000 miles. Or perhaps automobiles will have been immobilized for want of fuel.

Another question that should concern us is whether or not coal will still be available as a domestic fuel in, say, A.D. 2500—even assuming that industry has pretty largely converted to nuclear power.

We must face these pressing problems now, otherwise we shall deserve the opprobrium of posterity as thoughtless, wasteful and irresponsible people.

Partly to answer such questions about future power sources, R. C. Jordan and J. L. Threlkeld, both professors at the University of Minnesota, have made a thorough study of U.S. fuel reserves and draw the following conclusions:

More than 85 percent of all fossil fuels ever mined has been consumed since 1900. By "fossil fuels," Messrs. Jordan and Threlkeld mean deposits of oil and coal which required about 500 million years for their formation.

Another way of expressing their findings is to note that less than 10 percent of mankind consumes more than 50 percent of the fuels extracted from the earth. This consumption rate is rendered more alarming by the fact that oil and coal cannot be replenished, even in another 500 million years. Only wood—through reforestation—grows again.

Ironically enough, just as our fuel supplies are on the downgrade, all of the industrial nations report that their power requirements are increasing, and will continue to increase during the next few decades. For example, the United States expects its power requirements to be 45 percent higher between now and 1964. Japan heads the list in expanding power requirements, anticipating a fourfold increase in power consumption by A.D. 2000 over 1953 figures.

In 1952 the total world power consumption amounted to 10,200 billion or 10.2 trillion kilowatthours. Estimates based on Jordan and Threlkeld's findings are that in 1975 world consumption will be 27 trillion kilowatthours, and in A.D. 2000 this figure will have leaped to 84 trillion.

What power reserves will be available to meet these demands? At the Geneva Conference on the Peaceful Uses of the Atom in 1955, the following summary of world power reserves was published:

	Power reserves in billions of kilowatthours				
Country or continent	Coal	Oil	Natural gas	Hydraulic power	Power per capita 1,000 kwh
Africa	614			1.5	10
North America	12,406	50	66		75
Central America	26	3			2
South America	139	18			4
Asia	3,191	132		1.0	3
Europe	5,107	2	3		14
Soviet Union	10,447	16	10		53
Oceania	240				21

A further analysis of the data reveals that the per capita power reserves in Great Britain are 27,095 kilowatthours and in West Germany, 38,400 killowatthours. The situation is more favorable in smaller countries such as Iceland (40,000 kwh per capita), Norway (64,000) and Holland (51,200).

North America is far ahead of the rest of the world in power consumption as shown by the following table:

Country	Percent of World Power Consumption
North America	44.2
Africa	1.0
South America	7.1
Asia	10.7
Europe	24.5
Soviet Union	11.5
Oceania	0.9

COAL RESOURCES

The question again arises—how long will our coal supplies last? There is considerable difference of opinion as to the correct answer. One group of geologists, viewing with alarm the steadily increasing power requirements of modern man, warn that the world's coal resources won't last much beyond the end of the twentieth century. The Federal Geological Survey estimated the remaining coal reserves of the United States, including Alaska, at 1,660 billion short tons; at the 1958 rate of consumption of 369 million tons, this would mean that the U.S. reserves would last some 4,000 years. In Great Britain, the optimists estimate 250 years, the pessimists only 150 years. (The wide discrepancies stem from widely different estimates of consumption.)

Among the European nations, West Germany leads with coal reserves for 1,792,000 billion kilowatthours, or more conveniently 1.8 quadrillion kwh. Next comes Great Britain, with 1,368,000 billion kwh (1.4 quadrillion); France a poor third, trails with a mere 96,000 billion (96 trillion) kilowatthours of reserve.

On the basis of present consumption, if British coal reserves are supposed to be completely exhausted in about 660 years, those of West Germany will last approximately 860 years. Among many other technical factors, however, we must not overlook the fact that the exploitation of coal seams is becoming more and more difficult as time goes on. Fifty years ago the average mine shaft in West Germany was 1,150 feet deep; today the average depth is 2,300 feet. In some coal mines the working face is as deep as 3,000 feet.

OIL

The status of our oil reserves is substantially less favorable than in the case of coal. According to a 1960 report of the U.S. Bureau of Mines, the estimated proved reserves of world petroleum as of December, 1958, were about 273 billion barrels (of 42 U.S. gallons each). While this represented an increase of some 167 percent since December, 1951, the sad fact is that the demand is beginning to outstrip the capacity. The United States, which dominated the world's oil industry until about 1950 and produced more than half the world's oil, is now a net importer of crude petroleum, and the center of the world's known reserves has moved from the U.S. to the Middle East. The estimated U.S. crude petroleum reserves, according to the American Petroleum Institute and The American Gas Association, were 30.5 billion barrels as of December, 1958. At the same time the U.S. demand for petroleum products was 3.3 billion barrels a year—so that if the U.S. had to be entirely self-supporting in petroleum, it would have less than ten years' supply of oil left in all of its wells.

The U.S. Bureau of Mines report goes on to predict that by 1975 the total U.S. demand for petroleum products will be 17 million barrels a day, or 6.2 billion barrels a year. This compares with the 1961 world crude oil production of 8.2 billion barrels. "Total world crude oil demand will more than double by 1975," adds the Bureau of Mines. "As of 1960, world capacity is only 5 million barrels a day above present [1960] production of 18 million barrels a day. Oil will be plentiful for the next 15 or 20 years in spite of a great increase in demand. . . . In sight is the possible transportation of natural gas on a worldwide basis as a liquid carried in specially designed tankers."

The oil reserves of the Middle East are estimated by the same authorities as about 174 billion barrels, or about 65 percent of the world's reserves. Next comes the Soviet Union, with an estimated 27 billion barrels. Then Venezuela, with about 16.5 billion barrels. Note that at the predicted 1975 rate of consumption, Venezuela's reserves would be used up in less than three years if the U.S. had no other source of supply.

Western Europe's reserves are estimated at only 1.4 billion barrels; its production in 1961 (excluding Rumania) amounted to some 110 million barrels—about eleven days' supply for the oil-hungry U.S. if it were wholly dependent on Western European refineries. According to recent evidence of petroleum geologists, however, West Germany, which produces about 42 million barrels a year, may be able to stretch its oil reserves a little longer than previously expected. It is a noteworthy fact that West Germany, with its oil reserves representing 593 billion kilowatthours, has almost caught up with Rumania. The latter is, of course, the largest European oil-producing nation (86.3 million barrels in 1961) and has the largest European reserves (enough for 644 billion kilowatthours).

So far as the situation in other oil-producing countries is concerned, the outlook is not too bright. Although the proved reserves of the Middle East have increased 239 percent since 1951, the estimated 174 billion barrels would last the world only thirty years at the present consumption rate of 6.6 billion barrels; if this doubles or triples by 1975 as predicted, the 174 billion barrels of Middle East oil will accordingly last only about eight or ten years.

The productive capacity of the Far East—i.e., Indonesia and Borneo—may last for about twenty years; that of Africa, not more than ten. The oil reserves of the Eastern Block of nations are estimated to be good for about twenty years at the current rate of exploitation, which averages about 100 million barrels. The Soviet Union, according to 1961 estimates, produces 1.2 billion barrels yearly, compared with approximately 2.6 billion barrels produced by the United States in the same year.

All in all, the petroleum situation is alarming, since the world reserves remain fairly static while the world consumption increases in almost geometric proportion. The U.S. Bureau of Mines refers to U.S. increased consumption as "a constant compound annual growth rate of 3.71 percent from 1957." Up to now, the discovery of new oil reserves has been sufficent to counteract the recurring pessimism about the future oil supplies of the world. Although withdrawals from these reserves have increased from year to year, it has always been possible to offset them (as in the U.S., Canada and West Germany) by new discoveries which have occasionally amounted to as much as twelve times the current volume of production.

But the future of the world's oil supply, from the year 1970 on, seems to be largely a matter of chance.

Even if we take the optimistic view and extend the deadlines on coal and oil by a few more decades, we will still not have answered the question at the beginning of this chapter. Then what do we do for fuel? A forester can't afford to wait until the very last tree has been felled before thinking about reforestation.

WATER POWER

Water power is of considerable interest because there is little likelihood of its being exhausted in the next millennium or so. Surprisingly enough, however, water power accounts for only 1.8 percent of all existing power sources. Even in the vast Tennessee Valley Authority system embracing some twenty-five dams, the installed generating capacity of about 12 million kilowatts is only 34 percent hydroelectric, the bulk (66 percent) being generated in coal-burning steam power plants. Grand Coulee power plant on the Columbia River is the world's largest power plant, and its 1,974,000 kilowatts are all hydroelectric. Undoubtedly there are still many undiscovered possibilities in the field of hydroelectric power, and the dwindling of fossil fuel reserves makes it quite imperative to exploit "white coal" more than ever before.

TIDAL ENERGY

Although the energy of the tides is enormous, few of the experts specializing in new power sources have devoted serious attention to harnessing it. The tidal level at the mouths of the world's rivers varies in height, attaining a maximum height of 53 feet. There is an astonishing amount of kinetic energy in the rise and fall of tides. France is presently working on a huge tidal project, calling for the construction of a high-capacity power plant in Brittany. The first phase of the project will consist of a pilot plant capable of furnishing 700 million kilowatthours annually. If this works out as expected, the entire Bay of St. Michel will be utilized as a power source. Here the peak level of high tide is about 43 feet, which means that tidal energy would supply 17 billion kilowatthours a year—enough, for example, to satisfy 30 percent of the total power requirements of East and West Germany. Unfortunately, however, tidal energy for Germany has not as much promise as in other countries; for example, the difference in level of the North Sea and Baltic Sea between high and low tide is much less than it is on the French coast.

The well-known English scientist J. B. S. Haldane has voiced an odd warning about the use of tidal energy. In his opinion, the unlimited exploitation of tidal energy will slow the rise and fall of the tides, which in turn will seriously affect the earth's rotation. As a result, the days would become longer, the moon would approach closer to the earth, and the end result would be the cataclysmic destruction of our planet. Haldane figures that it will take about 36 million years for the earth to be destroyed in this way, so that we have a free hand for at least the next five or ten thousand years.

Seriously, Professor Haldane's unusual theory has been challenged on scientific grounds. A slowing down of the earth's rotation because of tidal friction would, it is argued, cause the moon to move farther away from the earth instead of approaching it, because the torque of the earth-moon system remains a constant. The moon would continue to recede from us until the periods of the earth's rotation and the moon's revolution were again of equal magnitude.

NUCLEAR POWER

Estimates as to how long the current "atomic age" will last have changed basically during the past decade. Whereas the early opinions were that there was a shortage of uranium deposits which would limit the atomic age to a few decades (according to authoritative U.S. experts), today the consensus is that the world supply of uranium and thorium, as well as other atomic raw materials, will last for roughly 2,000 years. This is the figure given by the contemporary British physicist Sir Charles G. Darwin in his highly interesting book, *The Next Million Years.*

Nuclear power, or atomic energy, today enables us to create wholly new and versatile industrial complexes and to open up power sources of practically unlimited capacity. Atomic energy is the most important supplement to the traditional types of power. But we must be soberly realistic about what we can reasonably expect in this field. Experience has shown that a nuclear power plant designed for an output of 50,000 kilowatts requires about the same capital investment as one that can deliver from three to ten times as much power. Consequently only large plants are feasible.

The effect of nuclear power on industry will be in every sense as dramatic as the effect of the steam engine or electric motor. Nevertheless, only the highly industrialized countries can meet the high cost of investment. Thus an equalization between the economically highly developed and underdeveloped areas cannot be expected at the outset.

THE SUN—OUR NUMBER ONE POWER RESERVE

Deprived as they are of nuclear power because of its cost, the underdeveloped countries are, paradoxically, very rich in an energy source overlooked by the industrialized nations—solar power. Exploitation of the sun's energy for man's use will be undertaken on an increasing scale in the course of the next few years. As we have noted, our knowledge of the use of solar energy is today at the stage where atomic energy was in 1945. It is by no means unlikely that in 1970 or 1980 solar energy will be receiving the same attention from engineers and scientists as nuclear power does today.

In our quest for power sources it is not simply a matter of how many tons of this or that kind of fuel is available. In many parts of the world the high cost of transportation makes the use of any fuel expensive—as is true of the coal deposits in Africa. A ton of coal, for example, costs about $30 in Nairobi, Kenya Colony and $27 in the Sudan; yet its price is a mere $2 or so in Capetown, and gets as low as 60 cents a ton in Witbank, Union of South Africa, although the quality is not of the best. The copper mines of Rhodesia have been constantly plagued by irregularities and uncertanties of coal deliveries. In Nairobi it takes about a half ton of coal to make 1,000 bricks—and, as we have seen, this means an outlay of about $15 for fuel alone, to say nothing of labor and overhead. By way of comparison, 1,000 common bricks in any local U.S. brickyard costs about $50, including fuel, materials, labor and manufacturer's, distributor's, and dealer's profit.

4 SOLAR MYTHS AND SOLAR POWER

Except for the present chapter, nothing we say about solar energy in this book comes under the heading of solar myths. It is interesting, though, when we take another look at the mythology of the ancient world, to find that the sun was one of the most dominant elements in that mythology. In a word, the sun was worshipped as the God of Life.

The cult of the god Ra in Egypt was, of course, out-and-out sun worship. The sun was the Supreme Lord of the land, and each Pharaoh was held to be the divine son of the sun and venerated as such. A number of different festivals in Ancient Egypt had their origin in sun worship.

In the mythology of India the sun is called Surya and is revered in the Rig-Veda under several other names, such as Savitr, the giver and sustainer of life, who awakens man and the universe every morning. The cult of Mithra, borrowed from Persia, was widespread in India at a very early date. Pusan or Pushan was the celestial shepherd god who protected both roads and cattle and guided the sacred flame on its perilous journey through the Underworld.

Among the non-Aryan peoples of India the practice of sun worship was even more widespread than among the Hindus. The Dravidians and Kolarians worshipped the solar disk under the name of Paramesvar, which meant Creator and Preserver. Images and symbols of the sun were displayed by bazaar owners and traders. The sun was invoked for the healing of all sorts of diseases, and impressive ceremonies marked the exorcism of devils, which involved partaking of a consecrated meal prepared without salt.

Yet today there are very few sun temples in India. The Temple of Komarak (Orissa), once an architectual wonder, now stands in ruins, bereft of worshippers. The sun temple at Gaya (Benares), however, still attracts crowds of devotees.

In Greece, the sun god had two names—Helios and Apollo. Plato speaks about a "pilgrimage to the sun." In Ancient Greece the cult of the sun meant worshipping the physical power of fire or flame, and the solar disk itself. No Grecian sun temples have survived.

During the classical era the name Helios was allowed to fall into disuse and the sun became identified with Apollo. The occurrence of the name "Helios Apollo" proves that an assimilation took place between the two deities. Apollo is said to have been an invention of the Stoics.

Helios appears in Greek mythology in the dual role of man and god. As a human being, he is a pretty disagreeable fellow— Homer tells us how he stole cattle from Zeus (*Odyssey,* XII). He is a symbol of brilliance and heat, of vitality and fertility; heat is the source of his strength (*Iliad,* XXII). Unlike the other gods who destroy men with their thunderbolts and arrows, Helios sends life-giving heat to the earth in the form of arrowlike rays. In short, Helios is the almighty one—*panderkes,* as Sophocles called him in *Oedipus Rex.* The famed Greek dramatist also referred to Helios as the god of fertility and the creator of harvests.

The rays of Helios have the divine power of either restoring sight or destroying it. Because Helios sees all, he is the judge and jury of all man's deeds and misdeeds, sitting at the right hand of Zeus the Father. He is singularly free of mortal foibles—more so than any of the other great Olympians. Identified not only with Apollo but with Serapis and Zeus as well, Helios attains the very highest rank of godhood. Pure white horses, symbols of heavenly light and purity, were sacrificed in his honor.

In ancient times Rhodes was called the "island of the sun." The remains of a huge solar temple still stand there today, on the site of the first town of Rhodes built in the fifth century, B.C. Here the yearly Festival of the Sun, known as the Halieia, attracted thousands to its sacrifices, games and processions. Part of the ceremony apparently involved driving a four-horse chariot into the sea.

Corinth, too, had its sun cult, the citadel of the city being dedicated to Helios. The story is that Helios won this prize after a big fight with Poseidon, god of the sea, but later on ceded it to Aphrodite, who shares with Amphititre the title of sea goddess. Sun worship was still being practiced in Corinth at the time of the Roman Empire; a statue of Helios adorned the temple of Aphrodite there. A number of sun temples have been found elsewhere in the Peloponnesus—at Elis, Trezene and Megalopolis, to name only three.

Did the inhabitants of Ancient Rome practice sun worship? Historians specializing in folklore and sagas believe that pre-Roman Italian tribes did in fact worship the sun. Emperor Augustus, after his conquest of Egypt, brought back two obelisks from Heliopolis and installed them at Rome, consecrating them to the sun. Jupiter (the Greek Zeus) was not only known as Jupiter Eternus but also as Jupiter Sol, the Sun God.

Turning to Japan, we find that the sun goddess played an important role in that country's mythology. The moon god is a very minor deity. Amaterasu, goddess of the luminous heavens, was worshipped as the creator of the Japanese island empire.

If space permitted, we could give dozens of other examples of sun worship from the cave ages to the Renaissance. Yet it is a curious fact that, with such abundance of sun worshippers, nobody in all that time seems to have hit upon the idea of using the sun as a source of power and energy. Apart from the burning glass of the Greeks, the only exception to the nonuse of solar energy were the practical experiments by the Hellenistic mathematician and physicist, Archimedes. We will have more to say about him in the chapter, "Pioneer in Solar Energy."

5 SOLAR PHYSICS

AND THERE WAS LIGHT

For untold billions of years, light (though there were no eyes to see it) was the only manifestation of energy in the universe. Sunlight, we are told, is a form of electromagnetic radiation resulting from the transmutation of helium into hydrogen and vice versa—a gigantic thermonuclear "bomb" in which matter is converted to energy. Light from such a source is what enables us to see or photograph the millions upon millions of stars, as well as the countless nebulae and diffuse clouds of hydrogen gas.

According to the "expanding universe" theory, the outer edges of the visible universe are constantly receding from us—from our 200-inch telescope on Mount Palomar and from the "Big Dish" radiotelescope at Jodrell Bank, England. And even apart from theory, the actual measurements of the universe in the past few years have indicated that it is many times larger, and much older, than we had reason to believe in the 1950s. (Opposed to the "expanding universe" theory is the "steady state" theory, which holds that the universe is not expanding from a primeval "bang" but in a continuous state of creation.)

About 1953 leading astronomers concluded that earlier estimates of the size of the Milky Way would have to be doubled. The Dutch astronomer J. C. Kapteyn (1851–1922) and the American Harlow Shapley (1885–   ) made numerous measurements of the Milky Way—our own galaxy—and came up with a figure of about 50,000 light years, a light year being the distance light travels in a year at 186,000 miles a second—some 6 trillion miles. But today astronomers hold that our galaxy is closer to 100,000 light years across, which is roughly 600 sextillion miles, or 6×10^{20} miles. The nearest known star, Proxima Centauri, is about 4.3 light years from the earth; the giant Betelgeuse in Orion is 200 light years away; and the great nebula in Andromeda, itself an "island universe" very much like our own Milky Way, is about a *million* light years away—an incomprehensible distance even though we can occasionally see this nebula with the naked eye.

Sirius, the Dog Star in Canis Major, is about eight light years from the earth, or about 50 trillion miles. Its light has to travel eight years to reach the earth. But if Sirius were as close to us as our sun, it would be forty times hotter on the earth than it is now, and we should not be writing a book about it. Many of the faintest starts in the heavens are vast distances from us, some up to 50,000 light years.

Any attempt to measure the size of the universe by stellar distances alone, however, is doomed to failure, for such distances merely reflect the incalculable vastness of the cosmos. Astronomers are continually discovering new nebulas, new constellations of nebulas or "supergalaxies," and there is even evidence of "super-supergalaxies," to say nothing of globular star clusters and shapeless yet gigantic masses of unconsolidated hydrogen gas.

For relatively near objects, such as stars in the Milky Way, or even "extragalactic" bodies such as the Andromeda nebula, the method of measuring (by parallax, using the diameter of the earth's orbit as the base) remains the same. However, according to the statement of Dr. Allan R. Sandage of Mount Palomar Observatory, some sort of correction seems required for measuring *very* distant objects. Dr. Sandage believes that the more distant galactic systems are up to *three* times further away than conventional measurements indicate.

Recent measurements seem to show that certain of the so-called "island universes," thought to be stellar galaxies, are nothing but clouds of glowing hydrogen gas. Others, however, can be resolved into stars by the 200-inch telescope.

How can light be "created" from hydrogen gas? Scientists tell us that the heat of the sun and other stars is not the result of ordinary combustion or chemical reaction, but of a large-scale thermonuclear reaction in which four atoms of hydrogen "fuse" to form one atom of helium, by means of a complex series of collisions at temperatures of millions of degrees involving carbon and nitrogen atoms as part of the cycle. In the interior of the sun, approximately 564 million tons of hydrogen are transformed into 560 million tons of helium every second; the remainder—4 million tons—is converted into the sun's radiant energy. A single gram of hydrogen gas in this process attains a calorific value equal to that of ten tons of coal. If we could harness the complete solar fusion cycle, a gram of hydrogen would heat our home all winter long!

The fact that thermonuclear reactions causes the transmutation of one element into another and releases a million times more energy than chemical reactions is the key to the puzzle of how the sun radiates such immense amounts of heat and energy without losing an appreciable part of its mass. The thermonuclear fusion process maintains a temperature of several million degrees in the sun's interior, and a temperature of about 11,000 degrees F on the apparent surface or photosphere.

THE SUN'S COMPOSITION

According to the "steady state" theory advanced by the British astronomer Fred Hoyle and others, there is a continual birth and death of stars going on in the universe. According to the "cosmic egg" and similar theories, all of the stars we now see in the universe were formed several billions of years ago, and number about 40 trillion. About two dozen stars disappear annually through explosion, disintegration or total loss of their hydrogen mass. The more hydrogen stars use up, the more their density increases while their luminosity decreases. Stars that have expended nearly all of their hydrogen and have very little luminous energy left are known as "white dwarfs."

Our sun is thought to be no exception to the rule of stellar evolution. Some authorities consider it to be about a third or half way through its life, and that it, too, will eventually become a white dwarf. Provided it doesn't became a "nova" first—or explode—which is held to be unlikely.

Early philosophers and astronomers had quaint notions about the sun's origin and structure. We have seen some of the solar myths of antiquity in the preceding chapter. Fire was strongly associated with the sun in the mind of primitive man. Babylonian and Egyptian astronomers seem to have been concerned more with the prediction of eclipses and other heavenly phenomena than with the acual composition of the sun. Similarly, the Greeks attempted to measure the sun's distance by means of their new science of geometry, or earth-measuring. Pythagoras and Plato pictured the sun as the Central Fire; Aristotle adopted this concept, but later Greek astronomers altered this to the concept that the sun revolves around the earth. Ptolemy, who lived circa A.D. 140, established this earth-centered astronomy, and refers to the sun only as a "fireball," being apparently concerned not with its composition but only with its apparent motion. As is well known, the Polish astronomer Copernicus, around the year 1500, announced the now well-proven fact that the sun is the center of the solar system.

The introduction of the spectroscope about the time of Huyghens and Newton (c. 1860) was a landmark in the development of our knowledge of the sun's interior. Before these famous scientists began their experiments with light, and before others like Fraunhofer, Bunsen and Kirchhoff made their discoveries relating to gas temperatures and color or spectra, our knowledge was actually a collection of vague speculations under the cloak of science. Nevertheless, since some of these old theories contained a grain of truth, it might be worth while retelling them here.

In 1760, Professor A. Wilson of Glasgow advanced the theory that the sun consisted of a black core surrounded by a luminous atmosphere (i.e., what we now call the photosphere), and that the sunspots he and other astronomers observed were "hollows" or holes in this luminous atmosphere, caused by the eruption of gases from the core.

Wilson's rather plausible theory was adopted and expanded by Sir William Herschel (1738–1822), who stressed the existence of the dark core and spoke about mountains and valleys on the sun, covered with extensive vegetation and inhabited by intelligent beings. According to Herschel, the sun had a warm outer layer which generated light and heat, and between this and the core was an additional layer of "cold" clouds which protected the plant and animal life on the surface from the heat welling up from the outer layer. The sunspots, Herschel agreed, were indeed holes in the surface, as Wilson had said.

Sir William believed, moreover, that the solar surface had a "wrinkled" appearance; that a very light gas emanated from the core which, under normal conditions, created the "pores" that Herschel had observed which we now call grains or nodules. (Bright streaks or shining spots on the sun are known as faculae.)

The Italian astronomer Pietro Angelo Secchi (1818–1878) believed that the luminous mass of the sun is merely a vast ball of gas, and that the grains or granulation we see on the surface is simply the outermost "shining" of the photosphere. Secchi also assumed that *above* the photosphere there was a "reversing layer" formed by metallic vapors from the "chromosphere," or "color sphere." Secchi, who was a Jesuit priest as well as astronomer, was a true pioneer in the exploration of the sun, and modern scientists have adopted his classification of photosphere, chromosphere, and reversing layer.

According to the French astronomer Hervé Auguste Faye (1814–1902), solar prominences are actually eruptions of hydrogen gas mixed with vapors of other solar elements, especially metals. This process, Faye believed, took place at temperatures higher than those in the upper regions of the sun. Faye's theory is still regarded today as a plausible explanation of solar prominences and of sunspots. Faye held that the photosphere is gaseous, supporting his opinion by the fact that the light radiated by the sun is not polarized; this could not be the case, as Arago proved, if the photosphere were either solid or liquid.

Faye disregarded the objections of Sir John Herschel (1792–1871), son of Sir William mentioned above, who pointed out that the lack of polarization could be explained by the fact that the solar surface is always in motion. The French scientist asserted that all solar matter is in a state of being split up or disintegrated, and that, in addition, the surface temperature of the sun is far lower than had been assumed up to that time.

The first theory of the sun's composition to be accepted as scientific as well as modern was advanced by the German physicist Gustav Robert Kirchhoff (1824–1887), who based his findings on spectroscopic analysis. In Kirchhoff's theory, the sun has a luminous central core surrounded by a cooler layer; the core must be either solid or liquid in order to produce the continuous spectrum which he observed.

Spectrographic analysis has provided valuable information about the composition and physical behavior of the sun. We owe to Sir Isaac Newton (1642–1727) the discovery that a beam of white light is dispersed by a prism into rays of various colors, and that under certain conditions the prism produces a rainbow-like spread of colors, the so-called solar spectrum.

Although Joseph von Fraunhofer (1787–1826) discovered the dark lines in the solar spectrum in 1814, it was not until 1859–60 —nearly half a century later—that Baron Christian von Bunsen (1791–1860) and Kirchhoff could explain this phenomenon. With the aid of spectrum analysis, Kirchhoff discovered the existence of various metals in the sun—sodium, iron, calcium, magnesium, nickel, barium, copper and zinc, together with others as outlined in the following table:

Elements	Bright lines in an arc spectrum	Dark lines in the solar spectrum	Observed by
Iron	600	460	Kirchhoff
Titanium	206	118	Thalen
Calcium	89	75	Kirchhoff
Manganese	75	57	Angström
Nickel	51	33	Kirchhoff
Cobalt	86	19	Thalen
Chromium	71	18	Kirchhoff
Barium	26	11	Kirchhoff
Sodium	9	8	Kirchhoff
Magnesium	7	7	Kirchhoff
Copper	15	7	Kirchhoff
Hydrogen	5	5	Angström
Palladium	29	5	Lockyer
Vanadium	54	4	Lockyer
Molybdenum	27	4	Lockyer
Strontium	74	4	Lockyer
Lead	41	3	Lockyer
Uranium	21	3	Lockyer
Aluminum	14	2	Angström
Cerium	64	2	Lockyer
Cadmium	20	2	Lockyer
Oxygen	42	12	Draper

Kirchhoff had demonstrated that a substance in the gaseous or vapor state absorbs precisely the same wavelengths which it radiates itself when incandescent. The sun has such "absorption spectra," too; consequently its surface must consist of incandescent solid and liquid materials; above it must be an atmosphere consisting of incandescent gases, since, according to the reasoning of Kirchhoff, Bunsen, Fraunhofer, et al., these produce an absorption effect on the white light radiating from the solar surface.

By measuring the absorption lines and comparing these with line spectra of known substances, scientists have gained a detailed knowledge of the nature of the sun's composition, as well as that of other stars. Spectrographic analysis shows that there are at least fifty-seven of the known terrestrial elements present in the sun. In addition, there are some peculiar combinations of elements which do not exist on earth—such as CN, CH, NH, OH, CaH, AlH, SiH, FeO and TiO. Spectrographic analysis further shows that hydrogen occurs twenty times more abundantly than oxygen on the sun.

Around 1870 the German physicist Johann Karl Zöllner (1834–1882) developed a theory about the sun which was based on Kirchhoff's ideas as well as on his own extensive observation. Like Kirchhoff, he insisted on the existence of a cold outer layer which produces the absorption lines, and believed that the photosphere consisted of a thin, fluid layer between a solid core and a gaseous, *luminous* atmosphere on the outside. According to Zöllner, the sunspots are the result of an uneven cooling of the solar surface, causing a kind of solid slag to form on the surface of the photosphere which shows up as dark spots. Gaslike streams were supposed to be forming toward the side of the colder regions of the core, and especially on the outer edge or limb of the sun. However, the modern theory of sunspot formation as expressed by the Russian-born U.S. astrophysicist George Gamow of George Washington University is somewhat at variance to this. According to Gamow, the sunspots and solar prominences are the eruptions of hot and luminous gases that "sometimes rise to a height of hundreds of thousands of miles above the sun's surface." Sunspots look dark, says Gamow, only because of their contrast with the more luminous surface around them. They are actually "great funnel-shaped vortices" in the outer layer of the sun. In these vortices the gases ascend spirally upwards and outwards. It is the expansion of these gases as they rise that decreases their temperature and make them seem darker than the rest of the solar surface.

Among other modern scientists, Charles Augustus Young

[23]

(1834–1908) of Princeton University should be mentioned. Young believed that the central part of the sun consists of a gas of immensely high temperature, the photosphere being only a cover of luminous "clouds" formed when condensable vapors cool off and condense on the surface, where they are exposed to the "cold temperatures" of outer space. The chromosphere, according to Young, is mostly noncondensable gases (hydrogen predominating) which remain after the clouds of the photosphere have been formed; in other words, the relationship of these gases to the photosphere is similar to that between oxygen and terrestrial clouds.

Sir Arthur S. Eddington (1882–1944), the world-renowned British astronomer, concluded that the sun consists of up to 35 percent hydrogen. Since hydrogen on the sun appears to be decreasing because of the conversion of four million tons of it to energy every second, it can be deduced that the total energy of the sun is decreasing as well. Gamow, however, is of the opposite opinion. While he recognizes the decrease in the sun's volume, and even claims that the radius of the solar sphere contracts every decade by 0.0003 percent (or about 1.2 miles), he asserts that its luminous energy is constantly increasing. Gamow explains this by stating that, in nuclear transmutations, the most important role is played by the temperature at which the reaction takes place—not by the number or amount of elements involved in the reaction. As more hydrogen is transformed into helium, the temperature of the sun's interior increases, so that solar radiation itself must increase with increased time.

Gamow's theory of a contracting solar radius and an increasing solar radiation is hardly cause for alarm, since such changes are imperceptible over long eons; solar radiation has remained practically constant during the past several thousand years. If it does increase in the future it will be extremely gradual, and will be more likely to benefit rather than harm the earth's plant and animal life.

Just the same, however, Gamow does talk about the eventual extinction of all life on the earth as the sun begins to "die" as its hydrogen is exhausted. This is not going to happen for some time, but "sooner or later, all the stellar supply of hydrogen must be finally exhausted." The big, bright stars arrive first at this stage of stellar evolution, at which point they begin to contract and loose their gravitational energy. This contraction leads to "general instability" and these stars burst into several smaller fragments. But our sun, says Gamow, is using its hydrogen supply very sparingly, is still "going strong," and is likely to live ten times longer than it has already. However, the sun is gradually becoming hotter and hotter, and may burn up everything on the surface of the earth several billion years from now, before it begins to contract. "As time passes, most of the stars belonging to the innumerable stellar islands grow older and older. And the year 12,000,000,000 after the Creation of the Universe, or A.D. 10,000,000,000, will find infinite space sparsely filled with still receding stellar islands populated by dead or dying stars." (*The Birth and Death of the Sun,* The Viking Press, New York, 1952.)

It will take billions of years, of course, before the earth's oceans and seas begin to boil from increased solar radiation. And when all the living creatures are extinct, the rocks of the earth's crust will still remain, a prospect that may give us some small comfort. Mankind a billion years hence will probably have migrated to some planet by means of vast spaceships capable of reaching a completely new solar system.

Simon Newcomb (1835–1909), mathematician and authority on the moon's motion and on solar parallax, believed that the sun would contract to half its present diameter in five million years, although its radiation would remain unchanged. It is difficult to see why Newcomb disregarded the effect that such a contraction would have on emitted energy, or why he limited the useful life of the sun—during which time it would deliver enough heat to make life possible on earth—to the relatively short period of 10 million years.

Hermann Ludwig von Helmholtz (1821–1894), who pioneered in the investigation of acoustical and electrical phenomena, was also an adherent of the solar contraction school, stating that it would take 9,500 years for the solar diameter to contract by one second of arc. Such a statement could be only theoretical or hypothetical, since it could not be experimentally verified in the foreseeable future. Like many similar prognostications, the predictions made by scientists as to the end of human life or the death of the universe make fascinating reading, despite the fact that excessive juggling with millions and billions of years is certainly done at the expense of scientific accuracy.

ARTIFICIAL SUNS IN THE LABORATORY

Thus far we have spoken about the heat energy derived from the hydrogen gas. How about the light, or luminous energy, which hydrogen can emit?

Research by P. Wildt and E. Vitense has explained the continuous solar spectrum necessary for the appearance of dark absorption lines. Their work, together with additional experiments with oxygen-arc light sources, proved that the continuous solar spectrum is produced by negative hydrogen ions—that is, by the combined effect of neutral hydrogen atoms and free electrons, whereby the latter either are attracted for a short while or pass by very closely to the hydrogen atoms. In 1952, Walter Lochte-Holtgreven and W. Niessen of Kiel, Germany, produced arcs about one inch long by electrical discharge in hydrogen at a pressure of 0.3–1 millimeters of mercury, 600 volts and 10–30 amperes (direct current). An increase in pressure did not prove to be of any advantage, and actually shortened the arcs to only a few millimeters. Experimental hydrogen-arc emissions like these constitute an authentic means of proving the current theory of solar radiation outlined above.

According to commonly accepted notions, the sun is the greatest source of heat and light that man has ever known. But actually there are stars that radiate far greater amounts of luminous and electromagnetic energy than our sun, although their effect is not felt on earth because of their vast distance. The example of Sirius has been already mentioned; according to Gamow, Sirius, which is "only" a half-million times further from us than the sun, uses its fuel fifteen times faster and will therefore "die" much earlier. Despite Sirius' far greater emission of energy and luminosity, the relative closeness of the sun means that we receive 13 million times more radiation from it than from the Dog Star.

MEASURING THE SUN'S LUMINOSITY

The luminous energy radiated by the sun was measured in 1725 by the French scientist Bourguer and again in 1790 by the English chemist William Hyde Wollaston. Both determined that the sun, at its zenith, illuminates a white surface about 10,000 times more than a standard candle placed at a distance of one foot. Thus the luminous energy or luminosity of the sun is said to be 10,000 foot-candles. Assuming that no absorption takes place in the earth's atmosphere, scientists have accepted the value of 10,000 foot-candles as accurate.

Because the distance to the sun is 93,000,000 miles, we have to multiply 10,000 by the square of 500 billion (the distance of the sun in *feet*), in accordance with the inverse square law of illumination. We thus obtain the number of candles required to give the same brilliance as the sun—in short, the sun's candlepower. It is 2.5×10^{27} or 2,500 trillion candles. This figure looks more impressive set in the middle of the page:

$$2,500,000,000,000,000,000,000,000,000,000$$

This truly is a fantastic number of candles, utterly inconceivable. (The standard candles referred to are "spermaceti" candles, each weighing 2.2 ounces and burning at the rate of 120 grains per hour.)

The foregoing experiments also determined that the sun's luminous energy is not uniform over the entire solar surface, but is strongest in the center, diminishing towards the outer edges.

THE SUN'S TEMPERATURE

Closely related to the foregoing discussion is the question of the sun's temperature. We will note how the several current theories on the subject differ in certain particulars.

First we may mention the French physicist Claude Servais Pouillet (1791–1868) and his pyrheliometric studies. Pouillet applied Dulong and Petit's law of radiation and determined the solar temperature to be between 2660 and 3200°F. Experimental observation, however, did not confirm these calculations; if, indeed, the sun's temperature were so low, various calorimeters used in melting heat-resistant substances with solar radiation would be faulty, since the temperatures reached in these processes are well over 5000°F.

Waterton and Secchi went to the other extreme. Basing their calculations on the law of cooling, they declared the temperature of the sun to be about 2,000,000,000°F. The Swedish scientist Ericsson's conclusion lay somewhere in between—about 7200°F.

(As we shall see later, he was fairly close so far as the *surface* temperature of the sun is concerned.) William Thomson, or Lord Kelvin as he was better known, tried to avoid both overestimates and underestimates. Although he founded the first absolute scale of temperature, named after him, we do not find statements from him about the possible range of solar temperature.

Returning to Pouillet, whose pyrheliometer, first of its kind, was a radiometer operating on the actinic principle—Pouillet established the solar constant of 1.7633 calories per square centimeter per minute. According to this constant, or variations of it to be mentioned later, the heat radiated from the sun's surface per square foot corresponds to the heat obtainable from burning three pounds of coal every two hours. If the sun is to be regarded as a heat engine, then, its intensity would be no more than fifteen to forty-five times that of a locomotive boiler, assuming uniformity of solar surface. According to this line of reasoning, the surface temperature would not be greater than two or three thousand degrees. No doubt Pouillet's results seemed quite logical to him.

The work of Pouillet was improved upon by his countryman Jules Violle (1841–1923) who, about the year 1876, took a step closer to determining the true temperature by acknowledging the fact that the solar temperature is not uniform on the surface or throughout the body of the sun. For his measurements he used an actinometer or improved pyrheliometer, which enabled him to determine the mean solar temperature at about 2700°F. Oddly enough, however, Violle stated that the measurements were in all probability too low, the true figure being more like 5400°F!

The Austrian physicist Joseph Stefan (1835–1893) discovered in 1879, and his countryman Ludwig Boltzmann (1844–1906) later proved theoretically that the energy radiated per second by a "blackbody" increases in proportion to the fourth power of the absolute temperature. This law, later known as the Stefan-Boltzmann law, made it possible to reach uniform results in solar temperature measurement. Stefan himself calculated the temperature of the sun at 11,700°F. This figure applies to the *photosphere,* which is the surface layer, but the temperature of the photosphere comes quite close to the "effective" temperature of the sun, regardless of how high the temperature of the core or center.

Other scientists came up with different figures: Wilhelm Wien's is fairly close to Stefan's—10,600°F; C. T. R. Wilson and C. Gray, 14,500°F; and Zöllner, previously mentioned, goes to the extreme figure of 50,000°F. According to Gamow and other contemporary scientists, the accepted figure for the *surface* temperature of the sun is about 6000°C or 11,000°F.

We should add the fact that the temperature of the sun must have remained fairly constant over the past several thousand years because there is no indication in all of recorded history to the contrary. The olive tree and grape vine still flourish today in the Middle East and Egypt as they did 2,000 years ago. To go much further back, however—to 6,000–10,000 B.C.—means a different story. Then the rivers of our planet were from 20 to 100 miles wide, drowning the now fertile valleys. The Rhine, for example, spread from the Black Forest to the Vosges. Conversely, during the Carboniferous Period, tropical heat prevailed in what is now the Arctic regions; during the glacial epoch or Ice Ages, the temperate zones were covered with ice several hundred feet thick.

These Ice Ages, however, were not related to changes in the amount of solar radiation, say today's scientists, but to possible shifts in the earth's axis, causing gradual but cumulative decrease in temperature during one part of the cycle and gradual increase in temperature during the opposite half of the cycle. These same scientists agree that a million years ago, before man arrived on the scene, the solar temperature was probably twice as high as it is today. This assertion is based on the application of formulas pertaining to solar radiation and temperature combined with recently discovered data on radioactivity. Another interesting calculation, generally accepted by scientists, is that the sun at about the time of its "formation" three or four billion years ago had a surface temperature of only 1600 to 2200°F—less than that of some terrestrial furnaces in use today.

On the basis of the fact that the earth's temperature is proportional to the sun's, it has been calculated that a decrease of 720°F in the sun's temperature would cause the mean temperature of the earth to drop from 68°F to 32°F—the freezing point of water—within a mere 200 years. But here again, let's not worry about the likelihood of this happening. Still another speculation is as follows: assuming that the temperature of the sun's interior is somewhere around 3.5 million degrees Fahrenheit (as modern scientists tell us), then it would take the sun about a million years to cool down the required 720°F—and the earth 66,000 years—before the mean terrestrial temperature would drop to 32°F.

Although the so-called "combustion" taking place in the sun

has been compared, throughout history, to that of a large block of coal, we know that such a notion is childish and misleading today. The process is not combustion as we know it on earth, but thermonuclear fusion and transmutation of elements. "We may describe the whole process," says Gamow, "as the transformation of hydrogen into helium as induced by high temperatures and aided by the catalytic action of carbon and nitrogen." A detailed account of these thermonuclear reactions in the sun is given in the following chapter.

MEASURING SOLAR RADIATION

Of the 3.79×10^{33} ergs per second radiated by the sun in the form of light, the planets and their satellites receive only 1/120,-000,000th part. The effective radiation of the sun can be measured by a special device known as the bolometer. Obviously only that radiation which is received by a small surface on earth can be measured directly, but since the surface of the earth and the extent of the solar system are known quantities, it is quite possible to calculate the entire amount of radiated energy.

The largest portion of radiation manifests itself in the form of light. For this reason it is assumed that light must emanate from the photosphere, which is only a thin layer of solar atmosphere, closest to the surface. When the temperature of solar radiation is being measured, the figures relate to the lower portion of the photosphere. Such temperature is called the "effective temperature," which we have given above as about 10,400°F.

The bolometer was developed and applied by three well-known solar scientists—Samuel P. Langley, Charles G. Abbot and F. E. Fowle. It is essentially a Wheatstone bridge, one arm of which consists of a thin foil which is constructed in the following manner: A thin foil of platinum is welded to a foil of silver, six times thicker than the platinum. Through continuous rolling and tempering, the silver foil is reduced to 10-micron thickness, with the platinum strip not thicker than 1 micron. This bimetallic strip is cemented to glass with Canadian balsam, then cut to a zigzag shape by means of a special tool. The balsam is then removed and the strip cemented to a recording plate with a solution of cellophane and ether. Then the connections are built in, and the parts protected by insulating with Japanese lacquer. Finally, the silver is dissolved in nitric acid. A zigzag path is thus generated from a 1-micron-thick strip of platinum. All the wavelengths of the spectrum will be absorbed by this strip, which is blackened with lampblack.

The measurements of solar radiation in all wavelengths thus obtained must be corrected for losses resulting from the reflection and refraction of the various rays through prisms, mirrors and lenses. The data obtained are then presented in the form of a curve showing the amount of radiation received per unit area of earth.

In order to arrive at the actual absorptivity of the earth's atmosphere, the following procedure is used: During the course of a clear day, a number of bolographs are obtained corresponding to various positions of the sun. In all of these bolographs the same region is recorded, and the ordinates of the resulting curves determine the amount of solar energy absorbed by the atmosphere. If this process is repeated for the entire spectrum, we can determine the relative value of the amount of radiation received from the sun by the outermost limits of the atmosphere.

MEASURING SOLAR HEAT

It is estimated that the heat radiated from the sun amounts to about a million kilogram calories per square meter of its surface per minute. This corresponds to about 40,000 watts per square inch of the sun's surface. If an attempt is made to generate such enormous heat or thermal energy by means of ordinary combusion, we would have to burn, according to Young, a layer of anthracite more than 16 feet thick with an area equal to that of the sun's entire surface—or about a ton per square foot of solar surface. This amount of coal would generate about 10,000 horsepower per square foot of the sun's surface. The earth itself receives only about 1/2,200,000,000 of the enormous heat radiated from the sun. (On very hot days this amount seems to be more than adequate.)

The method of measuring the increase in temperature caused by a specific amount of solar radiation on a definite area is called the "dynamic" method. Our friend Pouillet of a few pages back was the first to use this method, which requires much time and patience. Pouillet observed the temperature increase that occurred under the influence of sunlight within a definite time in a measured amount of water. The device which he used and constructed for the purpose was the pyrheliometer, previously mentioned. The physicist Crova used a similar pyrheliometer except that its upper receptacle was filled with mercury instead of water, and inside was an alcohol thermometer with a blackened bulb. Observations and measurements of solar heat and radiation are, for obvious reasons, best made on a mountaintop rather than in a valley.

In contrast to the dynamic method is the "static" method. The radiometer developed by Violle in 1877 known as the actinometer, and described in the *Annales de Chimie* for that year was first used for this type of measurement. Violle's device consisted of two concentric metal spheres, the diameter of the outer one being 9 inches and that of the inner sphere 6 inches. The outside surface of the larger sphere was polished, while that of the smaller sphere was blackened. The space between the two spheres was filled with water. The temperature is kept constant either by regulating the flow of water or by adding snow or ice. A thermometer is inserted into the actinometer so that the mercury bulb is located at the center of the inner sphere. Its stem protrudes from the actinometer itself.

Each of the spheres is provided with two openings so that a ray of sunlight can pass through the device. A reflector directs the sun's rays into the interior without striking the outer surfaces of the spheres. The heat received from the sun by the thermometer within the sphere must be equal to that which the thermometer gives off to the actinometer, so that the reading on the thermometer scale is an accurate, compensated measurement of solar heat.

The results obtained by either the static or dynamic methods are practically identical.

SOLAR CONSTANT

Aided by the foregoing measuring techniques, we can determine what is known as the "solar constant," which can be defined as the measurement of solar radiation in calories per minute per square centimeter of area perpendicular to the sun's rays. This amount of heat refers to the outer layer of the earth's atmosphere—not to the surface of the earth itself. The value of the solar constant varies somewhat, depending on the methods and calculations of various scientists, as indicated on page 164. The figure usually quoted is 2 gram calories per square centimeter per minute.

The earth's surface receives only part of the solar radiation that reaches the outermost layers of the earth's atmosphere. The radiation varies appreciably due to sunspot activity and other causes, but they do not exceed ± 1.5 percent.

Several scientists, among them Félix Trombe, present head of the French solar furnace program, differentiate between the real and the direct solar constant. The latter is the amount of heat received at a certain time on a certain spot of the earth's surface; variations of the direct constant are ten times greater than those of the "real" solar constant. The figures for the direct solar constant are substantially below those for the other constant, since much of the radiant energy is lost in the atmosphere.

The intensity of solar radiation measured on Monte Rosa in the Alps (elevation 15,900 feet, latitude 46°) was 1.77 calories; in Montpelier, France (elevation only 1,400 feet, latitude 44°) was 1.50 calories; and in Leningrad, Soviet Union (latitude 56°), 1.47 calories per square centimeter per minute.

The amount of thermal energy absorbed by the earth depends also on atmospheric conditions. Thus, water vapor absorbs some of the infrared rays and, to degree, the visible rays as well. Ozone in the atmosphere absorbs the ultraviolet rays and carbon dioxide the visible rays and long waves. Many kinds of dust and smoke particles in the atmosphere also decrease the amount of heat energy reaching the earth's surface.

MOTHER EARTH'S TEMPERATURE RISING

It is a recently discovered fact that the temperature of good old terra firma is unaccountably on the increase. No one has yet offered a good scientific explanation and many scientists are hard at work on the problem. In the first place, it has not yet been determined whether this phenomenon is caused by cosmic or solar effects. By means of simultaneous observations in different locations, aided by UNESCO and other worldwide associations for gathering scientific information, an attempt is being made to increase our knowledge not only of meteorological and climatic laws but also of the cosmic and solar influences and effects. Painstaking comparisons and correlations of observations and results are a necessary part of our combined effort to solve the problem.

Preparatory work in this direction was begun in 1955, when American scientists visited Antarctica on the icebreaker *Atka*. The intention was twofold—to find suitable starting points for future expeditions and locations for the erection of observation stations, and to carry out a series of preliminary scientific tests, especially in the geophysical and meteorological fields.

The reason for these large-scale efforts is the fact, as yet unexplained, that, according to the most precise observations, the temperature of the earth has slowly increased since about 1900—by 2.2°F in the past fifty years. A minor change, one might say, but one of this size is enough to perplex scientists who have been studying geophysics and cosmic rays for many years, because of what it might mean for human life in terms of a steady increase during the next 500 or 1,000 years.

According to one theory, changes occurring in the vast ice masses of Antarctica may be a determining factor in determining whether the observed temperature increase is worldwide or confined to one hemisphere. If ice is melting in the interior of this huge continent covering some 6 million square miles—the most colossal ice box in the world—at the same rate as ice near the coast, then scientists would conclude that the temperature increase is indeed global.

Some meteorologists hold that the answer lies in the slow change in the carbon dioxide content of the atmosphere. This gas is being constantly added to the air around us through the oxidation of the lungs, decomposition processes, industrial combustion processes, automobile and truck exhausts, forest fires, and various complex organic actions, not to mention volcanoes and other natural forms of combuston. Yet with all of these sources of increased carbon dioxide, it comprises only 0.03 percent of the earth's atmosphere, at sea level, compared with 78.03 percent for nitrogen, 20.99 percent for oxygen, and 0.94 percent for argon. The constant withdrawing of CO_2 from the air by plants and through the weathering of rocks and metals, as in the formation of limestone caves, does not appreciably affect its percentage composition. However, scientists are well aware that a very slight increase in this percentage—say from 0.03 to 0.045, a 50 percent increase—would raise the earth's temperature by as much as 1.8°F.

Having burned up about 100 billion tons of coal since 1900,

and equally huge quantities of petroleum and natural gas, mankind itself is at least partly responsible for the observed rise in the earth's temperature. Carbon dioxide combined with water vapor produces the well-known "greenhouse effect," whereby our atmosphere, serving as the roof of a greenhouse, allows sunlight to come in but tends to trap the heat radiation from the earth's surface. If the gases, such as CO_2, which are responsible for trapping this terrestrial infrared radiation are appreciably reduced, a condition like that of the Ice Ages threatens; if these gases are increased, the greenhouse tends to get hotter.

Scientists became aware of these factors once again when they observed that the Arctic ice pack is slowly melting away and its southern edge receding northward each year. Similar observations of the Antarctic ice pack are not yet available, because the extent and thickness of its immense ice masses are not fully known. However, it is estimated that there are between 6 and 12 million cubic miles of ice in this frozen continent, and should only a mere one percent of this ice melt, the water level of all the oceans in the world would rise from eight inches to three feet! Such a catastrophe would render thousands of miles of coastal land uninhabitable—to mention but one effect.

Slow-growing lichens that are found at the foot of glaciers in Queen Maud Land, Antarctica, prove that the continent's ice shelves have remained relatively stationary for many years. Future research will have to determine how and to what extent such isolated observations can be applied to Antarctica as a whole.

If the "carbon dioxide" theory should turn out to be erroneous, then the task of research will be to discover whether solar activity is responsible for the increase in our planet's temperature, and to what extent.

6 THERMONUCLEAR REACTIONS IN THE SUN

Besides the obvious question that scientific man has been asking himself for centuries—What keeps the sun going for thousands and millions of years without burning out?—there is the related question, What mechanism within the sun controls the thermonuclear transformation process itself? For the first question was answered conclusively by Hans Bethe and others about 1939, when it was shown that the sun was a gigantic thermonuclear reactor. The course of future research in solar energy should, it is argued, include efforts to obtain further scientific evidence of these thermonuclear reactions as well as methods of duplicating and utilizing a miniaturized version of such a reaction on earth.

As we have already indicated, energy in a thermonuclear reaction is released through the fusion of four hydrogen atoms with atomic weight of 1 each to form a helium atom with atomic weight of 4. The development of the hydrogen bomb was based on this principle, but the earlier atomic bomb, or uranium bomb, had to come first, since it must be used to "trigger" the hydrogen bomb. There is no other way as yet of providing the enormous heat which is required for the fusion of the four hydrogen atoms.

Actually we are not being precise when we speak of "hydrogen atoms" fusing to form "helium atoms" in the sun. At the extremely high temperatures at which fusion takes place (and solar temperatures reach 10 to 20 million degrees centigrade in the sun's core), matter no longer consists of atoms and molecules, but of bare nuclei, or atoms that have been stripped of their electronic shells by the great heat and enormous pressure. The speed, frequency, and persistency of such "thermal collisions" make thermonuclear reactions "infinitely more effective than ordinary bombardment processes," according to Gamow, who is credited with developing the theory of nuclear transformations in the sun.

When the helium atom is formed, it releases something like 20,000,000 electron volts; the formation of one pound of helium releases about 750,000,000 kilowatts of power, compared with only 75 million kw released when a pound of uranium 235 is "fissioned"—a ratio of about 10 to 1 in favor of thermonuclear energy. Or to put it another way: The amount of energy released by the splitting of all the atomic nuclei in one pound of U-235 corresponds to the heat energy of burning 12,500 tons of coal, whereas the formation of one pound of helium gives an amount of energy equal to that obtained by burning 125,000 tons of coal.

Theoretical proof of thermonuclear reactions in the sun was offered as early as 1929 by two young scientists, Robert Atkinson of the United States and Fritz Houtermans of Germany, based on the laws of kinetic energy and thermal motion. Nevertheless there were still a few renowned scientists, among them Sir James Jeans and Sir Arthur Eddington, who held to the "radioactivity" theory of solar energy. Ever since the discovery of radioactivity by the Curies about 1900, scientists have been intrigued with the analogy it presents to solar radiation, or vice versa; for example, it is well known that one grain of radium gives off 132 calories per hour, or 1,200,000 calories a year; multiply this by a few quintillion-fold, and you might have something like the intensity of solar radiation. What the scientists overlooked, however, is the fact that the release of energy by radioactive substances proceeds at a very slow rate compared to that encountered in chemical reactions. Actually, the energy of chemical reactions is measured in fractions of a second, while that of radioactivity is a matter of millions of years! Again, the sun would have to contain about 1.6 grams of radium per ton, or a total of 3.3×10^{27} grams, which is an unusually high proportion in relation to other solar elements as determined by spectrographic analysis. Moreover, we must not neglect the "half-life" phenomenon associated with radioactive substances; the activity of radium, for example, is reduced by one half at the end of 1,700 years.

Jeans and Eddington believed that light atoms were transformed into heavy, radioactive atoms in the interior of the sun as a result of pressures reaching millions or even billions of atmospheres. Today, scientists stress the importance of temperature rather than pressure in the sun's interior, pointing out that at a temperature of 200 million degrees centigrade, or 36 million degrees Fahrenheit, the average kinetic energy of thermal motion amounts to 5×10^{-9} erg, which is close to actual laboratory results of about 10^{-8} erg obtained during artificial transmutation of certain elements. Speaking of thermonuclear reactions, Gamow says, "all we need here is to raise the temperature of our mixture sufficiently high to get the reaction started."

The fact that high temperatures lead to the "ionization" or "stripping" of atoms means that the interior of the sun can be likened to a swarming mass of "naked nuclei" and free electrons. The degree of this atomic ionization and the speed of collisions both increase towards the sun's center. The thermonuclear reaction was described in 1938 by Hans Bethe (1906–   ) and Carl von Weizsäcker (1882–1951) (independently but simultaneously) as a "closed circular chain" or cyclic process—not a single nuclear reaction but "a whole sequence of linked nuclear transformations." Forever involved in this chain reaction cycle are the nuclei of carbon and nitrogen, which are continuously being regenerated, so to speak, changing from stable to unstable isotopes, emitting alpha or gamma particles, merging with free protons and splitting apart over and over again, but in the end serving only as "catalysts" in the main process—the transmutation of hydrogen nuclei into helium accompanied by the liberation of solar energy. (Radioactivity *does* enter into it, but not the way Jeans and Eddington thought.)

Ionized atoms, electrons and radioactivity thus take part in a cycle of continuous change inside the sun. But there is a fundamental difference between the behavior of atoms and electrons and that of solar radiation. Atoms and electrons are held within the spherical body of the sun by the force of solar gravity, which, according to Gamow, brought about the original rise of temperature to the value at which thermonuclear reactions could begin; also, electrostatic forces maintain a constant ratio between the number of nuclei and the number of electrons. Radiation, on the other hand, is directed away from the center of the sun, where its intensity is greatest, and towards the infinite reaches of outer space. The energy of solar radiation has been measured at 3.79×10^{33}

[38]

ergs per second, most of which goes off into space; the earth receives about 4.7 million horsepower per square mile, or 1,350,000 ergs per square centimeter per second. Stated another way, the amount of energy received from the sun by the earth each year is several million times the total world production of energy from the so-called fossil fuels.

The temperatures developed in the solar thermonuclear process have been estimated at around 45,000,000°F. Laboratory tests conducted in 1944 by G. Blanch, A. N. Lowan, Hans Bethe, and R. E. Marshall indicate a temperature as high as 47,000,000°F and a mean density 110 times that of water.

The mass of the sun is 1.985×10^{33} grams, or, in energy terms, 1.785×10^{54} ergs. When we subtract the measured amount of annual radiation (1.4×10^{41} ergs), we are left with a value that, when divided by the approximately 6 million seconds in a year, indicates that the sun ought to last about 15 trillion years at its present rate of radiation. (Gamow and others, however, have shown that long before this period is up the sun will have entered another stage in its evolution. First the radiation will increase about a hundredfold as the hydrogen approaches zero, then the sun will shrink rapidly in size, regaining its present luminosity in a few million years but at a greatly reduced diameter—about the size of Jupiter, in fact. And according to Gamow, all this will take place in a matter of several *billion* years hence—not trillion.)

Although Bethe's exploration of the carbon-nitrogen-oxygen-hydrogen-helium cycle as the source of solar energy has been widely accepted by astronomers and physicists, we may mention a few earlier or contrary theories for the sake of completeness. One of these sought to base the explanation of the sun's radiation mainly on helium; according to the calculations, however, the conversion of 1 percent of the solar mass into helium would release enough energy to keep the sun shining at its present rate for only a billion years. If oxygen were the main source of fuel in some sort of subatomic transformation, the sun would last 1.5 trillion years, according to another theory. A third estimate, based on the assumption that the sun contains 7 percent hydrogen, gives a life expectancy of 10 billion years. Mentioning these theories serves to point out that a good deal remains to be learned about the composition and atmosphere of the sun; nevertheless the details as worked out by Bethe in 1939 agree completely with the Einstein mass-energy equation, and the theory has been investigated and confirmed experimentally—not only by the hydrogen bomb itself but by the work of such scientists as C. L. Critchfield, C. Lauritsen, E. Salpeter, H. T. Stetson and S. B. Nicholson, to name but a few. As Gamow points out, Bethe demonstrated (using the figure of 1 percent carbon) that the energy of this chain reaction at a temperature of 20 million degrees *exactly coincides with the actual amount of energy radiated by our Sun.*" Since all other possible reactions lead to results inconsistent with the astrophysical evidence, it should be definitely accepted that *the carbon-nitrogen cycle represents the process mainly responsible for solar energy generation.*" (Gamow's italics, quoted from *The Life and Death of The Sun,* The Viking Press, New York, 1952.)

Let us turn now to other elements than hydrogen. Sir Joseph Lockyer (1836–1920) discovered helium in the solar spectrum before it had been found and identified on earth (by Sir William Ramsay in 1895). Its atomic weight is 4 and thus 4 atoms of hydrogen (atomic weight 1) may combine to form one atom of helium. The hydrogen atom itself consists of a positive and negative charge—or a proton as nucleus and an electron in a planetary orbit. Its diagrammed model has come to be a symbol of atomic energy.

One might think that all of the energy in the four hydrogen atoms would reappear in the newly formed helium atom, but this is not so; helium has a mass of only 3.97, so that a mass of 0.03 is lost when helium is thus formed. It is not actually "lost," of course, but transformed into energy.

What causes this energy to be released? Of the four electrons belonging to the four atoms of hydrogen, only two combine with the four protons to form the helium nucleus; the other two remain as planetary electrons. The .008 that we find in hydrogen's mass of 1.008 is the part that is "lost" in atomic transmutations involving hydrogen; an atom of oxygen, for example, can be formed from 16 atoms of hydrogen, but since the atomic weight of oxygen is *exactly* 16, the result is a loss of 0.008 for each hydrogen atom. The Nobel prizewinning English chemist Francis W. Aston (1877–1945) confirmed these figures, which have been approximated since 1900, through the use of his mass spectrograph in the 1930s.

Jean Baptiste Perrin (1870–1942), a French physicist who also won the Nobel prize, undertook similar calculations concerning atomic processes inside the sun; he also believed that solar heat resulted from the compression of lighter atoms into heavier ones.

He used the figure of 1.0077 as the atomic weight of hydrogen, and calculated that, since the atomic weights of oxygen, carbon, helium and hydrogen are 16, 12, 4, and 1.0077 respectively, the formation of either helium, carbon, or oxygen will result in the loss of 7.7 milligrams per gram of hydrogen, which are converted to $0.0077 \times 9 \times 10^{20}$ ergs or 166 million calories of heat energy.

The question obviously arises as to how each gram of the solar mass can radiate more than two billion calories—possibly more than 20 billion—without apparently affecting the total radiation. Perrin, long before Bethe and others described their theory of solar thermonuclear reactions, believed that he had found a satisfactory explanation. If the layer of the photosphere closest to the sun's surface should consist of hydrogen, then the compression of atoms alone would account for 180 billion calories, which, according to Perrin's calculations, would sustain solar radiation at its present rate for about 80 billion years, figuring two calories per year per gram of the solar mass as the present rate. To the eminent French scientist the matter appeared that simple. The trouble with the hypothesis is that it tells us nothing about the process of "compression," or what the "heavy atoms" are, or how long the process of compression will go on.

Einstein's celebrated formula, $E = MC^2$, gave the world a verifiable means of equating energy and mass, and summarized a theory that was proved experimentally every time a nuclear chain reaction was started or a nuclear bomb exploded. Since, as we have said, each gram of the solar mass emits such enormous amounts of energy, it is not too difficult to see that the formation of helium atoms can produce enough energy to maintain solar radiation for several millions of years, assuming no internal changes in the solar makeup.

Jules Henri Poincaré (1854–1912), author of over 300 papers in the field of physics and mathematics, attempted to prove that the sun's maximum future life was not more than 24 million years, but seems to have based his calculations on the assumption that the rate of solar radiation in the past billion or so years will remain constant throughout the entire 24 million years remaining; this, as we have seen, is not the generally accepted view today.

Geologists have taken another approach to estimating the age and future evolution of the sun. Basing their calculations on the present rate of sedimentation on land and in the oceans, they haves arrived at a figure of between 100 and 600 million years as

[41]

the time required for the earth's crust to form. Further, their findings indicate that during that period the intensity of solar radiation was fifteen times greater than it is today. Stated another way, the sun has lost 15 million "heat years" over a period of only one million terrestrial years. These findings lend support to the theory that the sun's formation was completed once it had reached its highest temperature, and that a general cooling process then set in. Again we must quote Gamow to the contrary, however; his detailed study of the future evolution of Sirius, our sun, and other stars in the same temperature-luminosity range (known as "the main sequence stars) led him to conclude that the sun's temperature and total radiation "are bound to increase while its hydrogen content diminishes. . . . The sun is slowly moving from its present position toward that of the hotter and more luminous stars."

7 PIONEERS IN SOLAR ENERGY

Archimedes, the greatest of Greek scientists (287–212 B.C.), seems to have been one of the first pioneers in the practical application of solar energy. According to the later Greek physician and historian Galen (130–220 A.D.), Archimedes, when he was superintending the defense of Syracuse during the siege by the Romans in 212 B.C., succeeded in setting fire to the Roman warships by means of a "burning mirror," mentioned in Galen's *De Temperamentis*. However, neither Plutarch nor Livy, who recorded how Archimedes used catapults and cranes against the Romans, tells us anything definite about this ingenious military use of the sun's rays.

Plutarch does report that at the time of Numa Pompilius (714–671 B.C.) the vestal virgins lighted the sacred fires with cone-shaped metal "goblets," which collected and focused the solar rays.

Almost eighteen hunndred years elapsed before a physicist took up where Archimedes left off. Athanasius Kircher (1601–1680), the first to repeat the Greek scientist's experiments with the burning mirror, had a more peaceful application in mind than the burning of ships. His efforts were directed at setting fire to a woodpile from a distance. Both Kircher's and Archimedes' methods for utilizing solar radiation are basically the same as those employed today; the burning mirror is still the simplest and most popular means of putting the sun's rays to work. About

14 years after Kircher's death two Florentine experimenters, Averani and Targioni, extended the field of solar application by attempting to melt a diamond with a burning mirror.

The German mathematician Ehrenfried Walter von Tschirnhaus, (1651–1708), member of the French Academy of Science, succeeded in melting ceramic materials with large burning lenses that he designed and built, ranging up to 30 inches in diameter— larger, in fact, than the lens of any telescope then in existence though not as optically correct. In 1699 the Duke of Orleans had one of these burning lenses or mirrors shipped from Germany to his court physician Homberg, who used it to melt gold and silver. A few years later the Frenchman Geoffroy continued Homberg's work by melting iron, tin, copper and mercury by the same method.

The achievements of the French in the utilization of solar energy received a big impetus with the work of the famed naturalist Georges Louis Leclerc Buffon (1707–1788), who in 1747 constructed a solar device containing as many as 360 plane mirrors. With a smaller arrangement of 168 plane mirrors, each about 6 inches square, Buffon set fire to a woodpile in the Royal Gardens from a distance of 200 feet. With his apparatus he was able to melt lead at 100 feet and silver at 59 feet. On the basis of these and other experiments, he concluded that Archimedes probably worked at a distance of between 100 and 140 feet when he set the Roman warships afire. For this and other scientific work, including the writing of his monumental *Histoire Naturelle* in 44 volumes, Louis XV conferred on Buffon the title of Count.

Claude Pouillet, the French mathematician and scientist already mentioned in connection with the pyrheliometer (page 28), estimated that the usable energy from the sun per square yard of the earth's surface between the equator and approximately 43° N or S latitude was about 1/6 thermal unit per second, which corresponds to nearly one horsepower.

Nicholas de Saussure (1740–1799), the well-known Swiss naturalist, constructed the first solar oven or "heat box." It consisted of five glass cubes, each cut in half and arranged so that adjacent flat surfaces were separated by an air space. De Saussure found that this air space considerably increased the heating effect, whereas the use of more than two glass layers did not improve the heat absorption and was thermally inefficient as well. The glass blocks were placed on a blackened table, enclosed in an insulated box, and thermometers were attached to each. The recorded temperature readings were 191°F. When the glass blocks were later coated on the side turned toward the sun, the temperature increased to between 230 and 320°F. De Saussure used this solar oven to heat food.

The burning mirror constructed by the French astronomer Jacques Cassini had a diameter of 3.7 feet and was known as the "Royal Mirror." According to the records of the Paris Observatory, it was presented to Louis XV in 1747. Cassini obtained temperatures of 1000°C (1832°F) with this mirror. He melted wrought iron in two seconds, and heated silver until it formed spidery filaments when plunged in cold water.

Sir Henry Bessemer (1813–1898) of steelmaking fame built a solar furnace in 1868 measuring about 10 feet in diameter and made up of a hundred separate reflector segments. Even though he succeeded in melting copper and zinc with it, Bessemer soon lost interest in this device, no doubt because of his greater concern with the manufacture of steel from cast iron.

A French physicist, C. L. A. Callier, published a number of works in the 1860s on the utilization of solar energy, and while they demonstrate considerable knowledge of the subject they do not describe any experiments by the author. And in 1872 an Englishman, Charles Wilson, constructed in Chile a solar-operated distillation device for purifying water, which is described later on page 51.

Also worthy of mention in this short summary are the unusual experiments of Stock and Heynemann of Germany. Their device concentrated the sun's rays to a focus inside a highly evacuated glass vessel, which contained a small magnesia crucible in which the substance to be heated was placed. They employed plano-concave lenses with a diameter of about 30 inches and a focal lenght of 20 inches. With this apparatus, Stock and Heynemann melted small samples of silicon, copper, cast iron and manganese.

As early as 1837 the English astronomer John Frederick Herschel, son of the German-born Sir William, traveled to the Cape of Good Hope in Africa and there built a small solar oven of mahogany, which he suitably insulated and then buried in sand, leaving only the top of it exposed. In this simple device Herschel successfully cooked meat and vegetables, recording an oven temperature of 240°F. The American scientist and aeronaut Samuel Pierpont Langley turned his attention to solar ovens in

1884, testing one of his own design on an expedition to Mount Whitney in California. Even with snow on the ground, Langley found that the sun heated his insulated box sufficiently to cook food at high altitudes. The increased heat loss due to lower air temperatures was apparently counteracted by the greater intensity of solar radiation at these heights.

Among solar energy pioneers who preferred the reflector system to the "heat box" or oven was Augustin Mouchot, (1825–1911), professor of physics at Tours, who began experimenting with reflectors in 1860 that lasted twenty years, supported by funds from the French government. He attempted broiling meat in the direct rays of the sun, but putrefaction of the surface resulted long before the meat was sufficiently cooked to be edible. Together with Abel Pifre, Mouchot later devised a metal reflector in the shape of a truncated cone, with glass tubes placed at the focal point and connected to a conventional boiler. In 1882 they put it to work with a steam engine, which in turn operated a printing press on the grounds of the Tuileries gardens in Paris. Appropriately enough the newspaper printed on this press was called *Le Soleil.*

Mouchot's reflector consisted of silver-plated sheet-metal plates, suitably mounted so that the entire device could be easily turned to follow the position of the sun. The collecting surface had an area of 40 square feet, and was connected to a boiler which received about 87 percent of the sun's heat. The steam engine to which the boiler was attached was, however, of very low efficiency. Whereas the boiler produced close to 7 pounds per hour of steam at atmospheric pressure (in Algiers during wintertime), the steam engine delivered only 2 horsepower, thus utilizing less than 3 percent of the solar heat received. This poor performance was not due to heat-transfer losses but rather to the inherent nature of the steam cycle. In his patent specifications, Mouchot called his apparatus a "solar pump."

Mouchot's book, *La chaleur solaire et ses applications industrielles,* which appeared in Paris in 1879, describes his many experiments in this field. It was the first scientific survey of the economic potential of solar energy, and as such may have stimulated his contemporaries to continue and expand his work.

The Swedish-American inventor John Ericsson (1803–1889), known to posterity as the inventor of the ironclad *Monitor* for the Union navy during the Civil War, turned from naval architecture to solar energy during the years 1868–1886. He made use of tubular boilers heated by concave mirrors, and produced enough steam to drive a 2½-horsepower engine, which was exhibited at several industrial fairs in New York State. Ericsson seems to have had a clearer conception about thermodynamics than many of his contemporaries, but unfortunately he did not publish the results of his work in harnessing the sun's rays.

Antoine Laurent Lavoisier, (1743–1794), founder of modern chemistry and member of the French Academy, made important contributions to the practical utilization of solar energy before the French Revolution put an end to his labors forever. With the help of the glassblowers of St. Gobain, Lavoisier obtained a double-concave lens measuring 51 inches in diameter, with a focal length of 10.5 feet. He filled this with alcohol to increase its refractive power and, focusing the sun's rays with it, he obtained temperatures high enough to melt various metals—even platinum, which has a melting point of 1755°C or 3190°F. In order to decrease the length of the solar machine, he installed a second lens with a 6-inch diameter, thus forming a compound lens system with a shorter focal length.

This brilliant French scientist concluded that the heat of the solar furnace was the purest one could find on earth. Despite his enormous contribution to both pure and applied chemistry, Lavoisier did not impress the Reign of Terror. In sentencing him to the guillotine, this revolutionary body declared that the Republic had no need for scientists. By fateful coincidence, the Terror ended in the same year.

William Adams built a solar "cooker" which used plane glass mirrors arranged in the form of an eight-sided pyramid, its larger diameter being about 28 inches. The mirrors reflected the solar rays onto a cylindrical cooking chamber enclosed in a glass vessel. Adams claimed to have cooked meat and vegetables in Bombay, India, with this device.

A California inventor named A. G. Eneas demonstrated in 1907 a well-designed solar generator which was operated for a time at the Cawston ostrich farm near Pasadena. A similar device was installed by Eneas in Arizona to pump water. In the latter installation the reflector was made of silver-coated glass plates, arranged on the inside surface of a truncated cone, the sides of which formed an angle of 45° with the axis. The larger diameter of the cone was 33½ feet. The lower part of the reflector was left open to reduce wind pressure.

Two other Americans, E. E. Willsie and J. Boyle, were the first to use, in 1918, a solar heater employing two circulating fluids. The heat of the sun was absorbed by a flat, glass-covered horizontal water tank and then transmitted to either ammonia, ether or sulfur dioxide in liquid form while the liquid was circulating in pipes surrounded by the water. When the ammonia or other liquid volatized due to the heat, the vapors, under pressure, were used to drive a steam engine. In its final form the tank measured nearly a thousand square feet, and the sun's rays could bring the water to the boiling point. It was found that liquid sulfur dioxide worked best, permitting the steam engine to develop as much as 15 horsepower at intervals, but even if this figure is accepted as correct the inefficiency of the engine (as mentioned above) precluded the wide use of this form of prime mover.

The renowned American authority on solar radiation, Dr. Charles Greeley Abbot of the Smithsonian Institution (1872–) has made many outstanding contributions to solar energy use. In 1940 he constructed an indirect type of solar heater for cooking, in which a liquid first absorbed the solar heat and then transmitted it to the cooking compartment. The solar reflector, which had an area of 300 square feet, focused the rays on a blackened metal tube in which the fluid circulated. In order to reduce heat loss from the surface, the metal tube was encased in a double-wall glass tube. The reflector had what might be called an equatorial mounting, in that it could be moved vertically and horizontally to follow seasonal and daily motion of the sun. To eliminate the need for pumps of any kind, the reflector was placed below the cooking chamber so that the heated fluid would circulate by gravity and thermal expansion. Despite the prestige of its inventor, this type of cooker never became popular.

One would think that sunny Italy would have produced a large number of solar energy devices and enthusiasts, but this unfortunately is not the case. Three Italian scientists deserve mention, however, beginning with Cesare Romagnoli, who in 1929 put solar energy to work for irrigation purposes, using an ethyl chloride motor driven by water power, the water having been preheated by the sun to a temperature of 55°C (130°F). Then we may note Professor Amelio of Bari, who in 1954 suggested the use of ethyl chloride to drive small turbines, and later put his theory to practical application in Libya. His method is said to reduce friction losses to a minimum and to achieve pressures higher than atmospheric. Finally we should mention the work of Enzo Carlivari, who used an ethyl chloride motor on the island of Ischia which developed 4½ horsepower, using water at the rate of 8.8 pounds per second at a temperature of 158°F. The solar motor ran at 8,000 revolutions per minute.

Apart from these modest beginnings, Italian research in this field would seem to have come to a halt, unfortunately, for the time being.

8 PRESENT-DAY USES OF SOLAR ENERGY

The practical utilization of solar energy today covers an extremely broad range of applications, from tiny watches to large metallurgical furnaces and from space-satellite transmitters to huge sea-water distillation plants. Somewhere in the middle of this scale of uses are the solar house, the solar cooker, and the sun-powered irrigation pump. In this chapter we will attempt to cover a representative number of these developments which hold so much promise for the future.

DESALTING OF SEA WATER

Extraction of salt from sea water goes back to prehistoric times. Early civilized man laid out shallow evaporation basins along seacoasts; sea water was led into these basins and evaporated in the sun until only a glittering crust of salt remained—the end product of the process, and a commodity prized by all primitive peoples.

But when the desired end product is the desalted water itself —either for irrigation or for drinking purposes—the process is much more complicated. Like Coleridge's Ancient Mariner, man has for centuries been chagrined by the fact that the vast, illimitable waters of the oceans are undrinkable, yet has continued to dream of ways and means that would make it potable. As world population increases and industry further raises the per capita consumption of water around the globe, serious water shortages loom on the immediate horizon. More than ever world leaders are turning to the desalting of water as perhaps the only long-term solution to this pressing problem.

In August, 1958, Dwight D. Eisenhower, then President of the United States, told the United Nations that "the ancient problem of water is on the threshold of solution." He referred to the fact that at that time more than 30 countries were engaged in research on the desalting of sea water by one means or another. The U.S. Department of Interior has been active in such development and research work since 1952. Working closely in cooperation with American firms like Westinghouse and Permutit, to mention only two, the Department has encouraged a variety of processes and supplied funds for the design and construction of pilot plants and specialized installations, which, in the aggregate, have produced up to 15 million gallons of fresh water from the ocean *every day*. In 1958 the U.S. Congress appropriated $10 million for the erection of five demonstration desalting plants—three for the conversion of sea water and two for the conversion of brackish water from salt lakes. At this writing, some of these plants are in full operation, but the results are not yet available in sufficient detail. The one obvious drawback is cost, which can run as high as $700 per acre-foot, compared to prices of from $2 to $10 for irrigation water, $10 to $44 for municipal water, and $50 to $100 for industrial water. But the history of technology shows that all new inventions or processes were costly at first, then grew less and less so with improvements and increased productivity.

While solar distillation of salt water is not the only method used in these and other pilot plants, it is by far the cheapest, since it eliminates most of the cost of electricity, chemicals, electrostatic or ionic filters and the like. The first solar distillation unit designed to provide a supply of potable water was built in 1872 in Chile, where the saltpeter miners had been faced with alarming shortages. Lack of drinking water was especially burdensome in the area of Las Salinas—literally, "the salt mines"—with its elevation of 4,300 feet and its great distance (75 miles) from the port of Antofagasta. The only available local water supply contained as much as 14 percent salt—which could only make the Chilean miners more thirsty.

A solar distillation apparatus consisting of 60 evaporators was constructed of wood, with a glass roof and iron pipes. The total area of the system, including piping, was 51,000 square feet, and the maximum daily yield was 5,500 gallons of distilled water, giving an average capacity of about a pound of water per square foot of surface. Taking into consideration the altitude of the site, it has been estimated that the incident solar energy was about 32,000 Btu per square foot, indicating an efficiency of 35 percent for the entire unit. Distilled water began flowing from the pipes each morning at 10 a.m. The average evaporation temperature in the tanks was 150°F with the temperature of the surrounding air at about 80°F when the sun was at zenith.

A smaller but more modern solar distillation plant has recently been built at Richmond, California, which has a maximum capacity of one gallon for each 9 square feet of evaporator surface per day.

The Mediterranean island of Pantelleria would likewise benefit from such an installation; in addition to plans for solar distillation there, two underwater conduits are scheduled to carry drinking water to Capri, Ischia and Procida from Sorrento, where a central plant will be built, instead of erecting separate installations on each of these small islands.

The need for solar distillation plants is unquestionable. In 1960 in the United States alone, about 330 billion gallons of water was used *per day,* which for a population of roughly 180 million means 1,834 gallons per person per day. It should be noted that in 1957 this figure was 1,475—making an increase in three years of *over 24 percent.* The U.S. Department of Commerce, moreover, has predicted that the total U.S. consumption by 1970 will be about 412 billion gallons; former Secretary of the Interior Fred M. Seaton predicted in 1957 that U.S. water needs will double by 1975—in other words, the per capita consumption will then be about 2,800 gallons per day.

Besides the United States and other highly industrialized nations, there are the numerous densely populated areas in undeveloped or emergent nations in such places as East, West and South Africa; West Pakistan; the areas along the Red Sea; Central America and the interior of Brazil; parts of Argentina and other South American countries—areas that have neither water nor fuel nor electricity for distilling sea water by conventional methods. Solar distillation would have the advantage of delivering adequate supplies of drinking water immediately when the sun is shining; properly designed storage facilities and plant operation would be sufficient to "carry over" on cloudy days. Even the Ancient Mariner, had he not been too preoccupied with the albatross, could have distilled enough water for the whole crew if he had used only half the ingenuity evinced by his more vigorous literary predecessor Robinson Crusoe.

Progress in solar distillation of water attracted a great deal of attention at the World Symposium on Applied Solar Energy in November, 1955, at Phoenix and Tucson, Arizona. Eight hundred experts from thirty-three countries—the largest group of scientists ever to convene on the subject—discussed the problems and prospects of applied solar energy. Among many other subjects covered, eight distillation projects were described. Two of them —one by R. P. Lappala of the Bjorksten Research Laboratory in Finland, the other by Dr. Maria Telkes, then consultant to the University of California—stirred up considerable interest.

The innovation demonstrated by Lappala consisted of covering the condensing surface of the distillation unit (which in this case measured 3 feet by 9 feet) with a thin film of polyvinyl alcohol in order to achieve a more "wettable" surface and thereby increase the rate and amount of condensation. (Other methods of achieving this result are by applying thin films of either albumen or gelatin.) To dry the coating thus applied, it is treated in turn with ammonium dichromate and subjected to ultraviolet radiation, a treatment that makes the polyvinyl alcohol insoluble. With this additional improvement, the solar distillation unit demonstrated was said to be capable of producing fresh water at a cost of about $4.00 per thousand gallons. For *drinking* water, this is an extremely economical price—less than half a cent per gallon, compared with the 30 to 40 cents a gallon one pays today for distilled water in five-gallon bottles.

In 1954 a systematic examination of all problems relating to solar distillation of sea water and other nondrinkable water was undertaken in Italy by the Institute for Market Research of Bologna and Bari Universities. Upon reviewing the work already done in this field, the Institute set about and began the construction of a number of mobile solar distillation units, together with the publication of all necessary information for their operation. There is no question but that the installation of these two types of solar units will go a long way toward solving the problem of diminishing fresh-water supplies in many parts of Italy.

One of these distillation units was built in Bari for experimental and test purposes. The unit, which weighed 330 pounds, had a daily capacity (on a warm and cloudless day) of about four gallons, enough for drinking and cooking purposes for the average family of four. The black-coated, rectangular ground surface of the unit had an area of 32 square feet; its glass roof, inclined on both sides at a 30-degree angle, had a surface of 54 square feet. In operation, radiation is absorbed through the glass window, causing the salt or brackish water to evaporate; the condensate that collects on the glass is collected in a bottle placed at the bottom of the unit—just about the simplest construction possible.

A larger distillation plant was built in Bari by Prof. Giorgio Nebbia in 1954. This unit had a total surface of about 120 square feet and held from 25 to 40 gallons of untreated water. Despite its larger surface area, it produced only about five gallons per day of drinking water, but its operation was simplicity itself, requiring only removal of the deposited salt and refilling with salt water every two or three days. Nebbia also claimed to have achieved excellent results when Plexiglas (acrylic polymer) was substituted for glass. Acrylic plastics are only very slightly affected by ultraviolet light, whereas other plastics like polyethylene and polyester film are gradually decomposed by it. Inhibitors or dyes that keep back the ultraviolet are now used by many plastics manufacturers for outdoor applications.

As long ago as 1888, the German inventor Theodor Ziem developed and patented a distillation method operated by solar energy but employing no reflectors or collectors of any kind; the fluids to be evaporated were subjected to the sun's rays directly. His apparatus consisted of a flat, boxlike container, the bottom and side walls of which were protected against heat loss by suitable insulators. The box had a glass roof sloped very gently at an angle of about 6 degrees. Vapor from the heated water condensed on the inside of this roof as the inside temperature rose higher than the outside—just as car windshields fog over on the inside on a clear sunny morning, except on a much larger scale. Ziem successfully applied this simple method not only to water purification but to the rectification of alcohol as well; four redistillations of 12 percent alcohol yielded 72 percent or 144-proof alcohol. The secret, of course, lies in how effectively the heat can be built up and retained (using the proper amount of insulation) while the liquid is being vaporized by the sun's rays; if the temperature difference between the liquid and the outside surface of the glass is not sufficiently large, condensation of the vapor will proceed at an extremely slow rate, and the drops may not be large enough to run off in any appreciable quantities. Ziem obtained an average yield of 1.6 quarts of water a day in Cairo; later, to obtain water in other arid regions, he placed strongly hygroscopic salts (calcium chloride, etc.) in flat, open vessels or basins to collect atmospheric moisture at night. This moisture was then distilled during the day by the direct-heating system just described, completing a cycle comparable to that found in nature itself—absorption, evaporation, and condensation. With such a rudimentary but foolproof device, one might cross the Sahara without fear of dying from thirst.

William Rhodes, of the West Laboratory in Phoenix, Arizona, using a basic design originated by Dr. Maria Telkes, devised a solar still made of stainless steel, with a 3-foot × 3-foot × 6-inch condensation chamber covered with glass and completely leak-proof. The unit employs neoprene pipes inside the storage tank, and, according to Rhodes, has a capacity of one gallon of drinking water per day. This well-built yet simple piece of equipment can be made to sell for about $70 (a similar model made of wood costs appreciably less), and since it requires neither gas nor electricity or other fuel its operating costs are insignificant.

With its vast areas of low rainfall and semiarid conditions, the Soviet Union might well be expected to concern itself with solar distillation and other water conservation techniques. With surprising candor, Dr. V. A. Baum, head of the Solar Technical Laboratory of the Krzishanovsky Power Institute in Tashkent, Turkestan (created in 1951), stated in his speech at the December 1954 meeting of UNESCO in New Delhi that there exist more than 400,000 square miles of barren wasteland in the Soviet Union, which represents about one-twentieth of the total land area of some 8.5 million square miles. He added, however, that extensive plans involving the utilization of solar energy were being made to convert these areas into fertile regions. Baum reported that parabolic reflectors with diameters of 33 feet had been developed in Tashkent, where they were being used for water distillation as well as for operating ice-making and refrigeration plants. He added that even larger installations of this kind were on the drawing boards, designed to supply water for the region around the Kara Kum desert in Turkmen Republic. In 1958 Baum again made the news by announcing Soviet plans for an enormous "helio-power plant" or solar-power station on the sun-drenched plains of Ararat, near the Turkish border, site of the legendary landing-place of Noah's Ark. Designed primarily to supply steam heating for a town of about 20,000 population, this power plant is described in its proper place on page 96 below.

While solar distillation plants play an increasingly important part in providing desalted water, they can be equally important in the field of salt recovery as well. Three-fourths of the earth's surface is covered to an average depth of 2½ miles with water containing about 3 percent of sodium chloride or common salt. Although there are large deposits of rock salt on land, obtained by mining or pumping, it is often more economical to obtain it by the evaporation of sea water.

On San Francisco Bay is located the world's largest solar-powered evaporating plant for the extraction of ocean salt—a coastal strip 40 miles long being permanently reserved for this process. The crystallization "season" begins here in April each year. Because ocean water contains other salts besides sodium chloride, these have to be removed by crystallization, settling or chemical extraction. Calcium sulfate, for example, is the first to be crystallized and allowed to settle. At this point in the process the salt content of the water has actually been concentrated from the original three percent to 25 percent.

This saturated solution is then pumped into watertight, clay-bottomed basins and exposed to the sun's rays. Calcium carbonate, magnesium chloride and certain salts of potassium are extracted during this phase by chemical and other means. Magnesium today is a very valuable by-product of the evaporation of sea water; one cubic mile of ocean water contains 12 million pounds of magnesium, or approximately 2½ pounds per ton of water. The magnesium salts and other by-products are sold by the Leslie Salt Company (owners and operators of this huge evaporation plant) to other companies, as Leslie is interested only in the final product—pure sodium chloride. When the solar evaporation process is complete, the resulting salt is 99 percent pure sodium chloride, with only very slight traces of other salts. An additional vacuum process refines it still further, so that the product you buy in the local supermarket is 99.9 percent pure.

When salt is extracted in this manner by solar energy, the efficiency of the process and the quality of the product depends on a number of factors other than the solar heat itself—such as the

A bulldozer tackles an enormous mound of salt reclaimed from the sea by solar energy. (*Leslie Salt Co.*)

Salt harvest at the Leslie Salt Company evaporation grounds along the eastern shore of San Francisco Bay. (*Leslie Salt Co.*)

Solar heating apparatus designed by Prof. Erich A. Farber of the University of Florida. A blackened sheet of aluminum inside each of the six glass-covered boxes serves as the heat collector. The boxes are angled to catch the vertical rays of the sun at zenith. (*University of Florida.*)

One of the efficient solar water heaters designed and built by the Radiasol Corporation of Casablanca. The glass-covered, insulated absorber unit has an area of 22 sq ft; capacity of hot-water tank is 53 gallons. With this simple device, residents of North Africa can have warm water during nine months of the year—a daily average of 40 gallons. (*Radiasol Corp.*)

flatness of the ocean bed, the correct amount of evaporation during the crystallization period, the average daily precipitation, and even the intensity of summer rainfall. Because these conditions are found in practically ideal combination in the San Francisco Bay area, nearly all of the salt produced in the United States by the solar-energy method is extracted there. The inexhaustible raw material of the ocean is either pumped into the evaporation basins or allowed to flow in by gravity.

From April to October the salt "grows" in the crystallization basins, reaching a depth of from 4 to 6 inches by "harvest time," which runs from the end of September to the middle of December. Instead of a reaper or combine, this harvesting employs power scoops on caterpillar treads, which load the salt on two-ton gondolas at the rate of about 25 tons of salt per hour. The 6-foot-wide shovels are adjusted and operated so that they harvest the salt without disturbing the sand or silt underneath. To transport the loaded gondolas, the company uses 26 diesel-tractors and 50 miles of tracks.

After transport from the bay area to the Leslie plant inland, the crude salt is again chemically treated in huge water tanks. The concentrated solution is boiled in special tanks about 20 feet high, after which it crystallizes once more, the salt being conveyed through rotary kilns until completely dry. From thence to the packaging room the remainder of the work is performed by automatic machinery, and eventually the transformed ocean salt reaches its ultimate consumer in the home, restaurant, or industry.

Unfortunately space does not permit telling a more detailed story of the desalting of sea water by solar energy. Since 1958 considerable work has been done in this field by such institutions as the University of California, the University of Florida, Georgia Institute of Technology, the Bjorksten Research Laboratories, Battelle Memorial Institute, the Office of Saline Water of the United States Department of the Interior, E. I. du Pont de Nemours and Company, and several others, as well as many individual engineers and industrial consultants.

SOLAR WATER HEATERS

How nice it would be if we could have all the hot water we wanted, without the need for an oil burner, coal furnace, gas, or electricity! Perhaps for those of us who live in winter climes, this

[57]

may never be a year-'round convenience, but at least in one quarter of the globe it is a working practicality. Today in many parts of North Africa, houses are equipped with solar-heated roof tanks that provide abundant hot water 300 days a year for cooking, washing, and other uses. One of the leaders in the field of solar water-heater construction is the Radiasol Corporation of Casablanca. A relative newcomer, this firm is now producing their ingenious and efficent device on a quantity basis. (Solar water heating was pioneered in Florida and California, then developed by Israel, the Soviet Union, and Japan. The latter country has probably the most active and growing group of supporters for this new-old form of heating.)

The Radiasol installations have the obvious advantage of extremely low-cost operation combined with low initial cost; besides eliminating the need for coal, oil or gas-fired boilers or electric heating coils, they don't even need pumps to get the water up to the roof provided there are existing pressure mains and suitable plumbing. (To provide hot water even when the sun isn't shining, Radiasol offers a combination electric and solar-energy heater which, even including the additional cost of the electricity, still affords a 90 percent reduction in costs as compared with conventional water-heating methods.)

The Radiasol water heater consists of the hot-water tank itself plus a glass-covered, insulated absorber unit with an area of 22 square feet exposed to the sun's rays. (The combination electric-and-solar heater has a 1,000-watt resistor and thermostat as well.) Capacity of the tank is 53 gallons. It is about 5 feet high, 6 wide, and weighs 390 pounds when empty.

These solar water heaters are generally connected with the existing plumbing, and while they are mostly installed on the roof of the house, they can be placed anywhere so long as they are exposed to the direct rays of the sun. The water temperatures reached in North Africa during a period of over nine months a year fluctuate between 104 and 122°F. Daily average supply of warm water during these 9 months, including heat loss in pipes from tank to faucets, is approximately 29 gallons for the 40-gallon model and 40 gallons for the 53-gallon size.

When larger quantities of hot water are required—as in industrial processes, for example—a number of Radiasol water heaters can be connected in series or "cascade." Hot-water installations of this kind, having a daily capacity of up to 1,600 gallons, are to be found in many North African hospitals, boarding schools, laboratories, barracks, and industrial plants. It is worth mentioning that because of the uniform heat distribution during the warming-up process, little or no scale builds up in the tank or pipes, even with moderately hard water.

SPACE HEATING WITH SOLAR ENERGY

As we have seen in earlier chapters, the world's supply of fossil fuels isn't going to last forever. The faster these supplies diminish the greater must be our efforts to decrease the amount consumed by households, for these are among the largest consumers of coal, oil, and natural gas. In some countries—notably the United States —households account for as much as 40 percent of the total national consumption.

One highly publicized substitute for fossil fuel, though still well beyond the realm of feasibility for the homeowner, has already been put to work to heat the huge plutonium works of the Atomic Energy Commission at Hanford in the State of Washington. Heating by atomic energy is what one would expect in such a plant, although when the plant was first constructed it had to rely on coal and oil. At Oak Ridge, Tennessee and Harwell, England atomic energy is also used for heating purposes. The systems in use at the latter two plants are of practical value only on a limited scale, and then only as a by-product of the generation of electric power. Nevertheless, the Hanford heating system does lend itself to large-scale industrial heating or cooling, being of a newer design than the first two.

The new atomic-power heating system operates somewhat as follows. Cooling water from the Columbia River is fed continuously into the Hanford reactors by means of a suitable pumping system. When the water in the reactor reaches a sufficiently high temperature, it is pumped into a heat exchanger, where it transfers part of its heat to an aqueous solution of ethylene glycol. The ethylene glycol, in turn carries this heat to the air-conditioning plants installed in the various buildings at Hanford where, with the aid of equipment operating on the principle of the heat pump (as in the ordinary household refrigerator), this heat is made to do the work of either cooling or heating.

After having yielded up most of its heat, the water from the river is stored in special tanks until its acquired radioactivity—picked up in passing through the reactor—has fallen to a safe level, after which it is returned to the Columbia River.

Ethylene glycol is used for the heat-transfer medium because of its low freezing point combined with chemical inertness; exposed pipes of the air-conditioning plant will not freeze even at temperatures as low as −40°F. As the reader probably knows, ethylene glycol is used as an antifreeze for automobile radiators. As a protective measure in the event of a possible break in the cooling-water pipes of the reactor, the ethylene glycol in the heat exchanger is kept under substantially higher pressure than the water that is fed into it. If a break does occur, nonradioactive ethylene glycol will flow into the radioactive water, and the difference in pressure will prevent the latter from escaping into the heating system.

According to the calculations of General Electric engineers stationed at the Hanford plant, the saving in fuel costs achieved by this heating system amounts to around $59,000 a year. These savings, however, must be viewed in the light of installation and maintenance costs, which are rather high; the initial outlay for the heating system was $614,000, and close to $500,000 more has been spent on maintenance up to the present writing. Which leads us to the subject of solar energy for space heating—a far less expensive proposition.

THE SOLAR HOUSE

The "solar house" began attracting attention in the United States in the early 1930s—the early years of the Great Depression, when wastefulness was practically unpatriotic, and the spirit of New England frugality was again abroad in the land. Solar houses, with their seeming promise of unlimited, year-'round, free heat if not light and power, caught the fancy of the public through Sunday supplement and homemaking magazines. (A dozen or so years later there would be a similar flurry of popular interest over the heat pump.)

The first solar houses in America seem to be those developed by Purdue University of Lafayette, Indiana, under the supervision of Prof. F. W. Hutchinson, which were equipped with oversize glass panes on their southern exposure—not much different from

[60]

This solar energy converter, which can produce about 20 watts of electricity under direct sunlight, is being used to power an automatic radio repeater station used by the U.S. Forest Service atop Santiago Peak in California. The solar energy converter is hooked up to a nickel-cadmium battery that stores the electricity on cloudy days. The converter was built and installed by Hoffman Electronics Corporation of Los Angeles.

Aerial view of the solar house at Phoenix, Arizona—one of the first in the United States in which solar heat supplies the entire heating requirements of the house. On the front of the roof can be seen some of the collectors, set at approximately 60 degrees, which consist of blackened aluminum sheet enclosed in two layers of glass.

Solar cooker designed for use in India has 38-in. chromium-plated reflector. Cooking vessel is fastened at focal point of reflector. The formula for the parabolic surface is $y^2 = 40x$. (*Indian National Physical Laboratory, New Delhi.*)

the enormous "picture windows" that are so commonplace in the 1960s. These Purdue houses, revolutionary enough for their day, were warm as toast when the sun was shining—even overheated, in fact. But when the sky was murky overhead, as Sir Harry Lauder put it, it was nicer to lie in your bed, and such houses required even more fuel than conventional models. Today our big picture windows, extending from ceiling to floor and down the full length of the living room, are actually double-walled plate-glass structures with controlled dead-air space between, providing as much insulation as the other three walls of the house.

Experiments with solar houses were also conducted by George O. G. Löf of the University of Colorado* beginning about the same time. Löf covered one third of the roof of his own house with a solar collector, through which air was caused to circulate before being blown into the house. With this "forced draft" hot-air system Löf achieved a 20 percent reduction in fuel consumption.

In the 1950s appeared the reports of solar heating experiments by Austin Whillier of the National Physical Laboratory in the Union of South Africa. In his later work Whillier used large-diameter collectors made of aluminum sheet, which was painted black. The heat absorbed by this collector was conveyed to an insulated heat accumulator tank, which then provided hot water for the heating system as well as washing and laundry purposes. The best location for this hot-water heat accumulator proved to be the ground floor, according to Whillier. The tank could be warmed either by the heated air from the accumulator area (circulated in an insulated duct), or by hot-water pipes built into the accumulator itself below the aluminum sheet. When the hot-air method was used, Whillier found that heat loss could be reduced by passing the air over heat-absorbing salts such as Glauber's salt (sodium sulfate, $Na_2SO_4 \cdot 10H_2O$—also known as "crazy water crystals") or disodium phosphate, $Na_2HPO_4 \cdot 12H_2O$. Although, as we shall see on page 65 below, Glauber's salt is used successfully in solar cookers, Whillier is of the opinion that these agents are unreliable as heat-transfer media and recommends the use of a hot-water system instead. He calculated the maximum amount of water needed for circulation to be 0.22 to 0.9 gallon per square foot of collector.

When used for heating houses, the heat accumulator tank

* Now Research Associate, University of Wisconsin.

should, according to Whillier, have a capacity of about 0.25 gallon per square foot of collector; could then be used during the summer for refrigeration purposes so that one would then have a low-cost, efficient air-conditioning system as well as a heating and hot-water system.

In California, the use of solar heating equipment has been quite extensive since the 1940s. In that traditionally sunny land of citrus fruits, oil wells, movie lots and climatic contrasts, solar heating is not confined to private homes but is now more and more widely used in public buildings such as schools, public baths, auditoriums or meeting halls, etc. The most popular type of equipment consists of heaters or collectors made of sealed, glass-covered boxes of shallow depth, containing rows of galvanized pipe of from ¾ to 1 inch inside diameter; a copper plate welded across the rows of pipe increases the heat absorption while at the same time passing the collected heat very rapidly to the pipe and thence to the water inside. Under favorable conditions of sunlight, this equipment produces hot water within a few minutes from initial exposure. The resulting hot water flows from the pipe into a 40 or 50-gallon tank, properly insulated, where it is either stored for subsequent use or conducted through fin-tube copper pipes for room heating. During the night the water cools only very little so that the rooms are warm in the early morning hours, and hot water is available for bathrooms and kitchen sink. As previously noted, equipment of this kind is frequently combined with "stand-by" conventional heating systems to insure a supply of heat and hot water in the event that the famed California sunshine is temporarily obscured—i.e., for several days in a row.

In Florida, Texas, and Arizona solar heating is achieved quite simply by placing a network of pipes on the roof of ranch-type homes, covering them with a glass enclosure which may also contain strips of cloth for better heat retention, and filling the pipes with water. Water temperature as high as 150°F are reached in a very short time, and the heated water is then conveyed to an insulated storage tank. Or the pipes may contain only heated air, collected inside the glass box by fans blowing over the heated cloth; the warm air may then be conveyed through pipes to a tank filled with rocks or gravel, which can hold the heat as long as four days. Thermostatic controls draw off and circulate the warm air whenever the room temperature drops sufficiently. There are numerous variations of this basic arrangement.

Today in the United States solar heating is no longer in the category of a fad, and construction of these and similar installations continues at a brisk pace. Obviously there are parts of the country where solar heating is unlikely to be widely used, if at all —the upper New England States, the states bordering on Canada, and, of course, the most northern state, Alaska; also, it is unlikely that large metropolitan apartment house buildings in smog-laden cities can look forward to wide application of solar heating. Nevertheless, a recent report by the U.S. Materials Policy Commission states that the expected sale of solar heating units throughout the country will reach about 13 million by 1975. The sale price of these units as projected into 1975 should be between $2,000 and $3,000 each, and the expected number of installations will account for about 10 percent of the combined power requirements of the entire United States. The Commission based its estimate on the assumption that the solar heating units of 1975 would be more efficient than those of today—particularly in the matter of long-term storage of solar heat for use during extended cloudy, rainy or overcast periods, and perhaps even through an entire winter.

THE SOLAR HOUSE IN MASSACHUSETTS

In 1958 the Massachusetts Institute of Technology completed a full-scale solar-heated house at Lexington, Mass., the fourth of a series of experimental solar-heating research projects first begun by MIT in 1938. This extensive program, which is still continuing at the present writing, was financed by a grant of more than $600,000 from Godfrey L. Cabot, a Boston businessman who, unbelievable as it may seem, was a member of the class of '78 and *nearly 100 years old* at the time the 1958 house was built. He was still hale and hearty in September of 1961 when Prof. Albert G. H. Dietz of the Department of Civil Engineering reported on the results of the three-year experiment at a United Nations conference on new sources of nonnuclear energy, held in Rome. Professor Dietz is a member of the space-heating committee of MIT's solar energy conversion project.

A collector, measuring 16 by 40 feet, was built into the roof of a conventional house in the Boston suburb, famed in U.S. history as the site of the American colonists' first turning back of the British army on April 19, 1775. The collector, set at an angle of 60°, consisted of two layers of glass, sandwiching a thin sheet of aluminum, which was painted black. Water, pumped through copper tubes attached to the aluminum sheet, was heated by the sun's rays, then stored in a 1,500-gallon tank located in the basement. Hot water from the tank was pumped through a heat exchanger to transfer the heat from the water to the air.

The warm air was then forced through ducts to heat the house, as described above in earlier installations, and as is done in most conventional hot-air systems. Incoming cold water from the public water system was heated for domestic use by pumping this "faucet" water through separate coils immersed in the hot water of the storage tank.

This uncomplicated heating system provided the occupants of the house with a comfortable level of temperature and an ample volume of hot water at all times, according to Professor Dietz. The house was occupied during the three-year experiment by Claremont D. Engebretson, chief engineer of the MIT solar project, and his family.

"The experiment's principal value," said Professor Dietz, "lies in the knowledge gained in constructing and operating a complex solar heating plant. Eventually, I believe, the sun's energy will be widely used as a fuel for heating systems. Meanwhile, solar energy in countries having abundant conventional fuels will be economically feasible only when the climate provides an unusually high yield of sunshine." (*New York Times,* September 3, 1961.)

On May 20, 1962, the *New York Times* ran another lengthy story on domestic solar heating, which is worth quoting in full:

An all-year home heating and cooling system that uses the sun as its main source of energy has been developed by two Illinois scientists.

Because many scientists believe that present sources of energy, including atomic energy, will some day be depleted, laboratories are trying to find ways to harness solar energy so fuels can be conserved.

The Illinois scientists believe that their development is a step toward solving this problem. The scientists are Kadaba V. Prasanna, a mechanical engineer at the Illinois Institute of Technology, and Dr. E. B. Penrod, visiting professor of mechanical engineering at the University of Illinois.

The system they devised uses two and one-half parts of solar energy and one part of electricity. A solar energy collector on a roof or wall, or both, together with a heat pump, can furnish most of the heat needed for an average home, they say.

If mass produced, Mr. Prasanna says, the cost of such a unit would be about 150 per cent more than that of conventional heating units. He adds, however, that the householder should save up to 70 per cent on fuel bills and would also have air conditioning in summer.

Under their system, a solar collector on a roof facing south would capture the sun's heat and transfer it to water circulating through coils leading into the ground, through the solar earth heat pump and then into the home's heating system.

During the evening, when the roof collector is useless, the water in the solar earth heat pump would be heated by solar energy stored in the earth during the day. There would also be excess heat circulated that had been stored during the previous day.

According to the scientists, the ground acts as a heat reservoir. They say this heat would be available during nights and cloudy days.

The solar collector is made of aluminum, the top of which is painted black to absorb the sun's heat. For water and space heating without a heat pump, a flat plate collector can be use, which develops a temperature as high as 195 degrees. For converting solar energy into power, a mirror is used that attains temperatures as high as 8,500 degrees.

Both men have designed solar collectors for space heating in experimental houses in various parts of the country. They report that the collectors work at high efficiency.

Mr. Prasanna notes that in the last ten years man has used more fuel to produce energy than he has used in all the previous centuries. He says that the system he helped to devise means that for every unit of electricity consumed, one unit of fossil fuel energy is saved.

The system devised by the Illinois scientist bears out the conclusions reached in a three-year experiment completed last year at the Massachusetts Institute of Technology. The experiment indicated that the sun can provide two-thirds of the energy required to supply heat and hot water for a three-bedroom house in New England.

The M.I.T. study said that full solar heating is feasible, but at present the cost of the equipment the system required is higher than can be justified by fuel savings.

A further disadvantage of domestic solar heating is that it is difficult to maintain an even temperature in the water storage tank. A few years ago Dr. Maria Telkes (page 53) tried to solve this problem by employing a chemical method for storing solar heat. She decided to use a compound that would melt and resolidify when exposed to a range of temperature between 90 and 100°F. She found that Glauber's salt, mentioned above on page 61, served this purpose adequately, since it is capable of storing 8.5 times more heat than water of the same volume when the temperature rises from 77 to 98°F.

In a solar house this chemical system works as follows: solar heat from the roof collector reaches hermetically sealed tanks containing crystallized Glauber's salt by way of air circulating in a duct system. These tanks furnish all of the rooms with a steady supply of warm air. Heat storage is achieved by utilizing the heat of fusion of Glauber's salt, which melts at a temperature of 90°F, and then releases the absorbed heat when it solidifies again. In this way solar heat can be stored for as long as 10 days, making it possible for the solar heating system to function not only overnight, but on cloudy days as well. Of further importance is the fact that the Glauber's salt remains chemically unchanged in the process, and rarely has to be replaced. The cost of materials in Dr. Telkes' installation, including the Glauber's salt, was approximately $3,000. The room temperature was regulated by thermostats, as indicated above.

SOLAR HEAT PUMPS FOR AIR CONDITIONING

The absorbing capacity of a solar heating system must be high, and its maintenance cost low, if it is to compete with conventional heating systems. With this fact in mind, Philip Sporn, president of the American Electric Power Corporation of New York, together with E. R. Ambrose, manager of its air-conditioning division, developed in 1950 a heat pump with a solar energy accumulator. The heat pump has been in use for many years—first in the ordinary household refrigerator, later as a device for pumping heat from the ground for domestic heating. The latter application has not proved to be economically feasible as yet, owing to the relatively high cost of the electricity required for its operation, although in some areas where the kilowatthour rate is low they have proved more efficient than conventional fuels.

The collector units employed by Sporn and Ambrose had four units, each 4 feet high and 7 feet long, placed on the roof in rows at a 50-degree angle. The compressor circulated the cooling liquid between the evaporator, the temperature of the latter being kept at about 60°F or higher. The liquid cooling agent was completely vaporized in the evaporator from heat provided by solar radiation. To complete the cycle, a condenser was used to turn the cooling agent back to liquid again, the heat thus given up being absorbed by the circulating water. The heated water was then fed into a tank and utilized for space heating as previously described.

In such installations the compressors must be of rather small size, to reduce heat losses that would greatly lower the thermal efficiency of the system. Experiments conducted in different areas of Ohio during 1955 showed that the solar heat pump operated 355 days out of the year, being shut down the other ten due to insufficient solar radiation. As a result of these and other tests the American Electric Power Service Corporation concluded that the future use of heat pumps built according to this principle can be expected to exceed that of conventional air-conditioning, although the word "future" was not clearly defined in terms of a definite number of years. There seems to be no reasonable doubt that sun-powered heat pumps can provide heat at substantially lower cost than those operating on traditional fuels, for the very obvious reason that there are no fuel costs involved whatever. Some American scientists believe that every house in the United States could be adequately heated by this method, provided that a heat pump, a sufficiently large collector, and a properly designed heat accumulator are combined in a unit engineered for the particular location and climate.

Turning from domestic to commercial installations of solar heating, it was reported in 1958 that an office building in Albuquerque, New Mexico, had successfully used solar heat *exclusively* for heating during the previous winter, and, according to its owners, "performed satisfactorily through the worst weather, a much cloudier-than-normal January." It was claimed to be the first office building in the world heated only by solar radiation. Engineers designed and built a flat-plate collector to heat the building, which transferred its heat to a 6,000-gallon underground water storage tank. The collector, inclined at a slope of about 6 degrees, formed most of the south wall of the building.

Italian solar-operated pumps of recent design range from $\frac{1}{10}$ to 3 horsepower. They are successful devices for pumping water in sunny, fuel-scarce regions if the temperature of the water being pumped and of that used in the condensing portion of the engine cycle is relatively cool. Pump efficiency falls off rapidly with water warmer than about 65°F.

The efficiency of any heat engine is inherently limited. The maximum efficiency of a device that performs work by utilizing the difference in two temperatures—such as those of steam and water—is fixed by the ratio of that difference in temperature to the higher temperature. This is the well-known Carnot cycle efficiency that applies to all heat engines.

A perfect solar engine, then, that receives heat at a temperature

250°F above its condensing source of, say, 65°F has a maximum efficiency of about 32 percent. Practical considerations, however, cut this at least in half.

In 1961 the Westinghouse Electric Corporation announced a 50-watt solar-powered water pump for use by the farmers of arid, power-poor nations. Westinghouse engineers told the United Nations Conference on New Sources of Energy, held in Rome in the late summer of 1961, that their pump could deliver enough water for irrigation and household needs of the small farmer. A 200-watt model, able to supply the personal needs of 1,200 persons, is also being built in a joint project with University of Wisconsin's Solar Engineering Laboratory.

SOLAR COOKERS

Of all the actual and possible applications of solar energy discussed in this book, it would appear that the simple, unpretentious solar cooker is the most widely popular. The average man is, or fancies himself, a lover of the great outdoors, and the suburbanite and apartment-dweller alike yield to the lure of camping or cook-outs at least once between spring and fall. Home barbecueing in postwar U.S. has blossomed into a multimillion-dollar business, with an estimated 12 million charcoal grills in use during 1960 and sales of barbecue equipment topping $100 million the same year. In that year, something more than 36 percent of all U.S. homes had either portable grills or outdoor fireplaces. Whether or not the solar cooker—which dispenses entirely with charcoal briquettes, starting fluids, and other paraphernalia so dear to the supermarket owner and his suppliers—will replace the outdoor grill is a prediction we would not venture to make at the present moment. There is, however, a combined element of economy and gadgetry about it, and the very least you can say about the solar cooker is that it doesn't smoke or scatter hot coals or embers.

One thing is certain, however. The solar cooker would be of enormous practical value in the so-called underdeveloped countries, whose greatest and most accessible natural resource is abundant, ever-present sunshine, but which are woefully lacking in conventional sources of power or fuel.

Several types of practical solar cookers have been developed during the past few years. To some extent these have been engi-

Commercial model of a small solar cooker developed in India.
(*Indian National Physical Laboratory, New Delhi.*)

A 44-in. square polished aluminum reflector collects the sun's
heat in this solar cooker from India. Parabolic formula is
$y^2 = 72x$. (*Indian National Physical Laboratory, New Delhi.*)

Not a new kind of child's swing, but a carefully engineered solar cooker with a 4½ × 9-ft polished aluminum reflector that can be rotated on its equatorial mount to follow the sun's movement throughout the day. Parabolic formula is $y^2 = 120x$. (*Indian National Physical Laboratory, New Delhi.*)

Dr. Maria Telkes demonstrating her 1954-model solar cooker at New York University—an insulated box with a glass face angled to the sun, on which four flat hinged mirrors reflect additional solar energy; this heat is then absorbed by Glauber's salt in the oven at the rear. Even before subsequent improvements, Dr. Telkes achieved temperatures from 300 to 440°F in this efficient cooker.

neered according to the most accurate scientific design calculations of thermal efficiencies and capacities. Construction of most of these solar-energy devices is based on the use of either concave or plane mirrors; they might be called solar houses in miniature, except that they produce higher internal temperatures and more concentrated heat.

Dr. Adam Tarcici of Beirut, Lebanon, has recently developed a very interesting type of solar cooker. His interest in solar energy dates back to 1943, when he was a student at the Sorbonne, and his knowledge of conditions in the Near East led him to concentrate more and more on the problem of providing the millions of people in those lands with a cheap, practical type of solar cooker that would go a long way to improving their diet and living standards. By 1949 he had constructed his first model in Nice, France. Although this early prototype was somewhat grotesque in shape, it worked and that was the main thing.

Since then Dr. Tarcici, now chargé d'affaires for Yemen in Beirut, has developed a whole family of models—23 different solar cookers in all. Six of his latest creations were exhibited in Tucson during the world convention of 1955 (page 53), while others have been duplicated and used in several countries of the East. In the past few years the Delta Mill Company of Cairo, Egypt, has been manufacturing on a mass production basis a compact, unitized solar cooker of Tarcici design, and the demand for it is steadily increasing. One of the many advantages of this model is it "collapsible" feature, which makes it readily portable, easily cleaned, and easily assembled for use at home or in work areas. Several American companies have shown interest in marketing this attractively designed and very practical device.

The dean of American solar-energy inventors, Charles Greeley Abbot (page 48) had, as early as 1936, built five "solar engines" that converted up to 15 percent of the incident solar energy into useful work. When he turned his attention to solar cookers, he pioneered with an entirely new principle. The concave mirror of his device was actually in the form of a cylinder (or half-cylinder) measuring about 2 feet in length. Its rated output was a mere $\frac{1}{50}$ of one horsepower, but in its ability to turn water into steam almost instantly, it was, according to Dr. Abbot, about three times as efficient as an ordinary coal-burning locomotive. The cylindrical mirror was mounted in an east-west position by means of a forked clamp, which as it slowly rotated kept the mirror constantly facing the sun. A high-vacuum tube, made of copper, was enclosed in a Pyrex tube and placed at the focus of the mirror. The copper tube, which was brightly polished at the top and blackened at the bottom, contained "Aroclor 1248," a special heat-transfer agent made by the Monsanto Chemical Company, a chlorinated biphenyl that is noncombustible and is easily pumped at room temperature but has a boiling point of 600°F and a low vapor pressure.

The Aroclor fluid, heated by solar energy, passes by gravity through the insulated copper tubes and transfers its heat to a heat exchanger, or tube bundle mounted inside a strong steel shell. Steam from this heat exchanger can be used to run a steam engine, or the heat can be used directly for cooking or industrial processing. The heat exchanger or "boiler" is well insulated, using the principle of the Dewar flask or vacuum bottle. Abbot's design is hardly recommended for home cooking, and its manufacture and use on a large scale in underdeveloped countries is out of the question, but if it could be combined with an abundant, inexpensive sun-storage chemical that would release a high proportion of its stored heat when desired we would then have the ideal solar engine with almost unlimited applications.

Practical, simplified solar cookers have reached their most advanced stage in India, where not only is there sufficient sun all the year 'round (as in other tropical countries) but the population is vast and constantly growing more so. In India the number of bright, sunshiny days far outnumber those married by fog, clouds or rain. Thus the heat storage problem there is not so pressing as it is in those countries where sunshine is intermittent. This fact, combined with the shortage in India of conventional fuels, makes solar heating and cooking an attractive possibility in this sprawling but progressive republic.

One of India's leading solar-energy scientists, M. L. Ghai, has described in a highly important technical paper the application of the solar heat box and the solar reflector to his country's needs. In the heat box the rays of the sun, although not so concentrated as in the reflector, are applied *directly,* whereas in the reflector the rays have to be first *concentrated* before they can be used for cooking or heating. In the design described by Mr. Ghai, the heat box consists of an insulated cubicle, painted black on the inside and covered on the outside with one or more sheets of glass. As all greenhouse operators know, window glass is an excellent transmitter of solar light and heat; the other design features of these boxes were based on experimental results of such practical inventors as de Saussure (page 44) and Herschel (page 20).

A portion of the direct rays of the sun is transmitted through the glass cover of the heat box, and absorbed by the black walls of the interior. Some of this absorbed heat is lost by reflection from the glass cover itself, while the rest is utilized to raise the temperature of the box—and of its contents, such as food. When the temperature of the interior increases, more heat is lost from the surface, a process that continues until equilibrium is reached between the two temperatures and the temperature of the food itself.

According to Mr. Ghai, the maximum temperature that can be reached in such a box is therefore dependent to a great extent on the insulation of the box itself. A heat box with a single sheet of glass as cover, but with little or no insulation on the sides, proved ineffectual as a solar heater because there was no heat accumulation or buildup inside the box; it was as though one would attempt to boil water by placing it in an open pot in direct sunlight. However, when two sheets of glass as used on the cover, the heat box does accumulate sufficient solar heat to reach the boiling point of water. A difficulty with all heat boxes is the fact that they possess, to greater or less extent, a *thermal inertia* that works to decrease heat buildup—the walls or sides of the box are themselves in the heating and cooling action, so that the incident solar heat cannot act instantaneously on the material to be heated.

Heat boxes that collect the sun's heat by means of horizontal covers (rather than by reflectors angled to face the sun directly) can't be used too successfully if the sun's altitude is not at least 65 degrees above the horizon. Even in India, the sun's elevation is right only for a few hours daily during the winter months. Longer hours of cooking, or an increase in heat buildup through more effective insulation, might give better overall efficiency, but even with these improvements the horizonal type of heat box would still need a minimum solar elevation of 40 degrees, which limits its use over wide areas of latitude.

The light-transmission factor for clear glass depends to a certain extent on its refractive index, its thickness, composition, and —to a larger degree—on the angles of incidence greated than 40 or 50° which it makes with the sun. At normal radiation incidence, the transmission capacity of glass plates 2 millimeters thick is assumed to be 0.86 for a single plate and 0.75 for a double plate.

The transmission capacity of two glass plates at angles of incidence of 45, 60 and 75 degrees is assumed to be 0.72, 0.65 and 0.35 respectively.

SOLAR COOKER WITH REFLECTOR

A solar cooker with a reflector has three distinct advantages over the horizonal heat box described above. First, the permissible range of the sun's elevation for efficient heating is substantially greater, meaning that it can be used longer each day and over a wider range of latitudes. Second, the reflector makes it possible to use a solar cooker in the early morning or late afternoon hours, whereas the flat horizontal cook box is limited to the midday hours when the sun is at or near zenith. Third, the heat box has a relatively high thermal inertia, whereas the reflector-type cooker starts operating almost immediately as soon as it is exposed to the sun.

The reflectivity of silver-plated reflectors is as high as 96 percent. Aluminum or anodized reflectors have a reflectivity of between 70 and 85 percent, depending on the purity of aluminum, the graininess of the aluminum film in the case of anodized sheet, the surface hardness of the aluminum alloy, and other factors.

A reflector with an effective surface of 10 square feet absorbs a total of 1,000 watts of incident energy. According to information from the designer, the radiation received by the cooker described on page 74 is about 655 watts. The higher the temperature rise in the device, the greater is the heat loss at the surface, as previously noted. A noninsulated cooker produces about 409 watts, compared with 572 watts for an insulated one.

CONSTRUCTION OF REFLECTORS

Spherical or parabolic reflectors provide the maximum concentration of radiation in solar engines or cookers. Spherical reflectors with a large bending radius must, when applied to solar cookers, be equipped with a device for supporting the cooking compartment at exactly the right distance from the geometric center of the reflector, otherwise the compartment will not be "in focus," and the rays will be spread out over too large an area to provide maximum heating of the box. When the image area is large, it frequently happens that the bottom of the cooker (if it is of normal size) gets out of focus, so that frequent adjustment of the reflector becomes necessary. Some models are equipped with automatic devices for keeping the food compartment continuously in focus.

A parabolic reflector does not have these disadvantages, since the image it produces is clear, small and sharp. The astigmatism of the parabolic reflector is greater than that of the spherical reflector, but because the image is so much smaller, it stays in focus much longer. For this reason, as well as for the fact that it is much easier to handle, the parabolic reflector must be considered the better of the two types.

Next to its corrosion resistance, the most important property of a reflector is its reflective power. Some data on the reflective power of various materials are given in the following table:

Material	Reflectivity, percent
Aluminum, high-purity	89
Aluminum, commercial grade	74–85
Chromium	51
Constantan (60 Cu, 40 Ni)	64
Copper, polished or burnished	82
Duralumin	53
Glass, silvered	88
Magnalium (69 Al, 31 Mg)	74
Mercury-bismuth amalgam	72
Nickel, polished	60
Silver-plated metal (electrodeposited)	96
Speculum (68 Cu, 32 Sn)	66
Steel, soft	58
chromium-plated	54
galvanized	64
silver-plated	91
tinned	49
Zinc, polished	54

Aluminum foil, which besides being inexpensive has a high reflectivity (70–85 percent), did not prove successful as a coating for reflectors, perhaps because of its much greater heat absorption and transmission.

As we have mentioned earlier, solar reflectors must be mounted so as to follow the sun. This means not only the sun's diurnal motion across the sky but also its annual movement in the ecliptic, or apparent yearly path in the skies northward and southward through the celestial equator—involving a constantly changing zenith distance or "high point" of the sun each day.

In a locality of L degrees latitude, the reflector must be rotated from north to south from $L° + 23\frac{1}{2}°$ to $L° - 23\frac{1}{2}°$. For example, at the latitude of New Delhi, which is $28\frac{1}{2}°$, the sun at zenith during the summer (high noon) will be only 5 degrees from the celestial zenith or point directly overhead. The reflector surface must therefore be positioned almost horizontally. In the winter, however, the angle of the sun at high noon is $28\frac{1}{2} + 23\frac{1}{2} = 52°$, meaning that the reflector must be inclined 52 degrees from the horizontal in order to be perpendicular to the sun's rays. The maximum adjustment in the east-west direction (from rising to setting sun) is theoretically 180 degrees, but in practice this becomes 90 degrees, covering the effective portion of the sun's daily motion.

The solar engine or cooker, unlike the astronomer's telescope, does not have to be so precisely mounted as to follow the movement of the sun *exactly*. The sharpness of focus can vary from a half inch to an inch one way or the other—a range of accuracy provided even by mass-produced parabolic mirrors.

The design and construction of the cooker or food compartment will depend on the effective surface and reflectivity of the reflector. If the reflector surface is small, then the amount of heat focused on the cooker will not be enough to make up for the heat losses, and the temperature will not build up sufficiently for cooking purposes. A larger reflector surface means that the capacity of the cooker can be increased, but as with everything else a point of diminishing returns is soon reached, where the reflector becomes either too unwieldy or too expensive to construct or to mount.

A surface of 6 square feet with a reflective power of 75 percent has been found to be the minimum size for cooking purposes under favorable conditions of sunshine, air temperature and velocity of air movement. The efficiency of reflectors with a surface of about 10 square feet is, of course, much higher. The optimum size of reflector surfaces for solar cookers seems to be about 12 square feet. This is sufficient for cooking an average meal for five or six persons, more if necessary, depending on the bulk or quality of the food.

FOCAL LENGTH OF SOLAR COOKERS

Since, as we have just seen, the cooking compartment must be designed according to the size of the reflector, it follows that the focal point, or focal length of the reflector, also affects the design. Focal lengths greater than about 3 feet are not practical due to random energy losses. Reflectors with focal lengths of between 10 and 30 inches were used in the tests conducted by the National Physical Laboratory of New Delhi; and it was determined that a focal length of about 18 inches was most appropriate for reflectors having an effective surface of 10 square feet.

In considering the question of focal length, one must keep in mind that the cooking compartment has to be kept level, regardless of the changing position of the reflector—unless the chef wants to wind up with an *olla podrida* or mulligan stew. In the summertime, when the altitude of the sun is close to 90 degrees or directly overhead, the rays will reach down into the bottom of the cooker; but in the forenoon or afternoon, these rays will strike the inner walls at varying angles, heating the upper layers of the food more than the bottom layers, thereby causing some dissatisfaction among the guests. To correct this condition, the reflector must be turned the proper amount while the cooker itself remains in a horizontal position. A parabolic mirror or reflector with a diameter of 3½ feet and a focal length of 18 inches can be rotated through an angle of 28 degrees, which in most latitudes is ample to correct for the sun's angle of elevation.

Where local conditions or the type of reflector make it impossible to direct the sun's rays perpendicularly into the cooking chamber so that the heating effect is reduced, it will help to provide a blackened surface on the inside bottom of the compartment in order to increase its heat-absorbing capacity. Brass, copper and steel can be blackened electrolytically, or a coating of high-heat resisting, nontoxic paint can be applied.

A number of experiments were conducted by Mr. Ghai in India to determine the amount of time required for cooking various meals under different conditions. A quart of water, exposed to the sun at 12:30 P.M. on a cloudless day in May, took 20 minutes to reach a temperature of 190°F; on the same day, with the same cloudless sky but at 11:00 A.M., the time required to reach the same temperature was 22½ minutes.

DR. TELKES SERVES A SOLAR LUNCH

New York in November is usually cold and gray. But this particular November day, when a small group of people gathered for lunch on the terrace of New York University's Administration Building in Washington Square, the sun was warm and bright, like the conversation. For this was no ordinary lunch the guests were looking forward to. Although the hostess, Dr. Maria Telkes, then of the NYU College of Engineering research staff, was outwardly calm and relaxed, her guests were excited and curious. This was to be their first "solar meal."

"The sun is really cooperating today," Dr. Telkes remarked as her guests gathered around a large, shiny aluminum box standing on a small wooden table on the terrace. "I don't think we're going to be disappointed."

The "box," or solar cooker, was in the shape of a right prism, its frontal plane making an angle of about 45 degrees with the base. Four hinged aluminum reflectors, looking like the opened covers of a shipping carton, were extended to catch the rays of the autumnal sun at noon. The guests, comprising a number of well-known scientists as well as research students, could see a black-enameled heat absorbing plate on the inside back wall of the box. Below, but visible only from the back, was the glass-wool insulated "cooking cell" or food chamber, in which the savory meal was now simmering. The tantalizing aroma of that favorite American dish, hamburgers and onions, arose from the odd-looking contrivance, unsullied by the acrid odor of burning charcoal. For this was out-door cooking by the purest kind of heat known to man.

"Yes, you can call it a fuel-less barbecue, I guess," said Dr. Telkes, who had designed this magic box, as well as many of its predecessors. "Or you might call it a stove that cooks by harnessing sunlight. You can see that it cooks, all right, and it certainly is a simple, uncomplicated device that even a child can handle safely. This model—or an improved version of it—is a really practical thing, something that can be used by every housewife at one time or another. In fact, I really think there will come a day when millions of families all over the world—" Dr. Telkes paused abruptly, then added with a smile, "There I go again, making a speech. I know you didn't come here today to listen to a speech. You must be hungry!"

Dr. Adam Tarcici of Beirut, Lebanon, demonstrating his simple parabolic-reflector solar cooker.

Dr. Maria Tekles (left) and assistant demonstrating her latest (1962) model solar cooker—a box surrounded by eight flat hinged reflectors instead of four as in the earlier model. Oven temperatures of 400°F are easily attained in the new model.

Overall view of the Convair solar furnace at San Diego. In ideal weather, this 10-ft-diameter solar furnace can reach a temperature of 3230°C (5846°F). The sun's rays are collected by the parabolic aluminum mirror and come to a focus in a point the size of a dime. (*General Dynamics Corp.*)

Solar energy installation in Algiers. The apparatus is kept inside the hangar in bad weather.

After a little more stirring and turning of pots and pans from behind the shiny box, the great moment of unveiling arrived. "You may come around here, now, and take a look before we're served," said Dr. Telkes. Peering inside the cooking chamber from the rear, one could see a large iron skillet containing eight or nine sizzling hamburgers smothered in onions, flanked by two steaming aluminum double-boilers—one filled with creamy mashed potatoes and the other with mixed vegetables.

"There must be a hidden electrical cord somewhere," one guest remarked. "The sun couldn't have done this all by itself!"

"Or maybe a can of Sterno with an invisible flame," his female companion giggled.

When the food had been served, buffet style, the doubting Thomases were the first to congratulate Dr. Telkes on her culinary skill. "Simply marvelous!" "Cooked to a turn!" and "Better than Schrafft's any day!" were some of the offhand compliments bestowed on the genial lady inventor.

After the guests had settled comfortably indoors with their coffee—which had been brewed in an electric percolator as a concession to vested utility interests—Dr. Telkes returned to the scientific aspects of her unusual but tasty luncheon.

"New York sunshine isn't the most intense in the world," she said, "yet today, with an outside temperature of about seventy degrees Fahrenheit we were able to get an oven temperature of nearly three hundred and fifty degrees with our little solar cooker here. In other countries, where the sun shines more strongly, as in the Near East, or in most parts of Africa, we know that the same type of solar cooker will reach as high as four hundred and fifty degrees Fahrenheit."

Dr. Telkes said that the design was especially suitable for cooking all kinds of vegetables and other foods that required boiling, such as rice.

"Today we had enough heat for our needs," she added. "But sometimes it will be necessary to develop more heat 'buildup,' or thermal storage, either because of local conditions or the kind of meal you're preparing. All you need then beyond the equipment you saw outside, is a small amount of Glauber's salt. Most of you gentlemen know this substance well, and how it can serve as a heat-storing agent. It helps build up the heat at a faster rate, and allows the oven to hold the heat for as long as an hour after sundown. And you can purchase enough of it at any chemical supply house for a dollar or so."

In answer to the obvious question about how long it takes to prepare a meal in a solar cooker, Dr. Telkes replied: "The hamburgers usually take from twenty to thirty-five minutes, depending, of course, on how thick or large you make them. The potatoes and vegetables are usually done in the same amount of time."

Had she cooked other types of dishes in the solar cooker?

"Oh, yes, many different types. We have made beef stew and lamb stew, and we have made some very delicious roasts, and we've even broiled chicken in the model you saw. Most roasts, as you know, need only about three hundred and twenty-five or three hundred and fifty degrees, a medium roast of beef needing only a half hour or so. A pork shoulder takes a litle longer, as is true for any boned or rolled roasts. We have cooked all kinds of fish, and of course soup is no problem at all. We have baked cakes, too, although this requires some previous knowledge of the art of baking. We've had great success with everything. No complaints from anyone about flavor, or raw spots."

Despite these excellent results, however, Dr. Telkes modestly admits that her device needs further improvement. "The model we used just now is still an experimental type. When it's been perfected a bit more, it may then be ready for large-scale mass production. We think it could be made to sell for five dollars or less. And then, think of how many millions of people could use it all over the world—people who either can't afford conventional fuel, or simply can't obtain any!"

Dr. Telkes is not alone in her enthusiasm for solar cooking. The Ford Foundation in 1954 made a grant of $45,000 for the development of her solar cooker, and other groups, including the University of Wisconsin, the University of California, and a number of manufacturing concerns, have followed her work closely. There is nothing visionary about the undertaking; in fact, the outstanding feature of Dr. Telkes' solar cooker is its great practicality and usefulness.

SOLAR FURNACES

Straubel's Pioneering Work. Rudolf Straubel, one of Germany's most distinguished scientists and from 1903 to 1933 the successor to Ernst Abbé at the Carl Zeiss Works in Jena, constructed in 1921 a large solar "melting oven," or solar projector-reflector, which had a diameter of 6½ feet and a focal length of 3 feet. Straubel was looking for a new source of heat that would produce extremely high melting temperatures for advanced metallurgical work, one that would be "purer" than existing arcs or furnaces which contaminated the metal with foreign matter and extraneous gases. Solar heat—the kind we get from an ordinary burning glass or hand lens, but on a much larger scale—seemed to be the only answer.

In his apparatus, the solar beam was reflected from an auxiliary mirror through a tube with an inside diameter of 12 inches, which projected from an opening in the main convex mirror. At the receiving end of the tube a 6-inch lens of short focal length served to focus the rays. An ingenious mounting enabled the device to follow the sun's movement, tilting the mirror automatically to keep the sun's rays perpendicular. (Unfortunately, the arrangement was such that the crucible tilted, too, so that the molten metal dripped out over the sides at the wrong time.)

Straubel was able to melt a $\frac{5}{16}$-in. iron rod at the focus of his solar furnace in a matter of two or three seconds. Not satisfied with these results, however, he improved his invention in 1933 by constructing a parabolic mirror of the same dimensions and focal length as the first, but with a vertical instead of equatorial axis. This kept the crucible horizontal and eliminated the spilling of molten metal, but made necessary the addition of a second mirror with a plane surface and diameter of 8 feet, which could be moved automatically to reflect the sun's rays onto the parabolic mirror. The entire installation, though bulky, was simple enough in operation. The material to be melted, usually in rod or strip form, was placed at the focal point and moved horizontally through the focal point at a uniform speed, depending on the rate of melting. Under favorable conditions of air temperature and sunlight, Straubel's furnace attained temperatures of as high as 7000°F—nearly 60 percent of the surface temperature of the sun itself!

Parenthetically, it is of interest to note the behavior of materials during the solar melting process. Magnesium oxide reacts with extraordinary intensity, and melts within 10 seconds. Other substances, such as thorium oxide, are crystallized before melting occurs, while a number of other oxides tend to sublimate—that is, to pass directly from the solid to the gaseous state. Oxides with high melting points, such as aluminum oxide (corundum, Al_2O_3), used for abrasive wheels in toolroom grinding, is sometimes hurled out of the crucible by the sudden elevation of temperature, which "explodes" the air contained in the crystals.

Conn's Solar Furnace for the Silicate Industry. Straubel's work on solar furnaces was further developed by the American scientist William M. Conn of Kansas City, Kansas, who applied the solar furnace to research in metallic oxides and ceramic materials for the silicate industry. In 1954 Conn constructed at Rockhurst College in Missouri a parabolic aluminum mirror with a diameter of 10 feet, which yielded temperatures up to 3700°F. All of the know elements could be melted in it, including carbon and tungsten compounds, but the biggest use of Conn's furnace proved to be in the silicate industry, where the purity of the high-heat source is of the greatest importance to the finished product. According to Conn and others, the solar furnace would seem to be the *only* source of high temperatures that should be used in the making of refractory materials, not only because of the purity of the heat source but also because conventional furnaces—either electrical or open-hearth—designed to achieve the same high temperatures would be too costly to construct. The solar furnace, in addition, provides a fast, unform melt completely free from gas or soot accumulation.

The tests conducted by Conn involved (1) heating and cooling the sample according to a predetermined cycle; (2) keeping the sample at a constant temperature for a considerable length of time; (3) measuring the temperature of the sample, and (4) observing directly the entire process of heating, melting and cooling.

Conn's solar furnaces have openings of 5 and 10 feet, with focal lengths of from 26 to 36 inches. The approximate diameter of their solar images or focal points varies from ¼ to ⅜ inch.

Samples of aluminum silicates were prepared in the form of refractory bricks from standard commercial raw materials. These were dried in a gas-fired oven and baked in a large Denver or tunnel kiln. An analysis of the raw materials is given in the following table.

The foregoing table shows the considerable variation in the composition of these raw materials. For test purposes the samples were cut into small blocks measuring about 2 inches square by 3 inches deep. Their clay content varied from 16 to approximately 70 percent.

Asbestos gloves protect this Convair–General Dynamics engineer as he examines hole burned in ceramic test block at focal point of 10-ft diameter solar furnace, San Diego. (*General Dynamics Corp.*)

Steel rod becomes white hot in a few seconds in the Convair solar furnace at San Diego, designed and built by William M. Conn of Kansas City. Here we are looking through the opening in the reflector as a technician places the rod in the crucible located at the focal point. (*General Dynamics Corp.*)

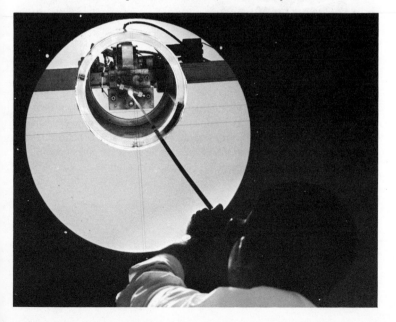

A technician atop a service vehicle surveys the heliostat, a heat-collection device with 355 adjustable mirrors that convert sunlight into a high-temperature beam. This 1,440-sq.-ft. heliostat is one of four major components of the large solar furnace built by the United States Army at Natick, Massachusetts, in 1958.

Contained oxides or alkalies	No. 801 Lincoln clay No. 1–6	No. 808 Porce- lain clay	No. 815 Sheet corun- dum	No. 817 Silli- manite	No. 820 Argilla- ceous sand	No. 837 Kyanite (India)
Al_2O_3	35.20	47.33	99.64	68.73	0.19	68.50
SiO_2	57.11	50.58	0.02	30.50	99.76	30.28
TiO_2	0.89	0.94	0.01	0.73	0.03	0.67
Fe_2O_3	2.51	0.15	0.08	0.04	0.02	0.28
CaO	0.48	0.53				0.17
MgO	1.25	0.47				0.10
Alkalies	2.57					

Summary of Conn Experiments. Test specimens in the form of rods or bars were placed in the crucible with the surface of greatest area turned toward the reflector. Before actual melting is attempted, the sample is held in a slightly out-of-focus position to permit gradual preheating, the length of time being dependent on the type of material. The sample is then moved into sharp focus for the melting operation.

If the sample or specimen has to be kept at a specified temperature for a determined length of time, the focus has to be adjusted from time to time in order to compensate for changes in solar brightness, atmospheric haze, or other changes that might occur. This, of course, is one of the unpredictables of solar heating; a thin cloud cover or a ground fog can upset the best-laid plans of scientists and metallurgists.

During Conn's experiments, the temperature was controlled with a high degree of accuracy—a variation of only plus or minus 2°F over a temperature range up to 3600°F being achieved over long periods. Even higher temperatures, as measured with an optical pyrometer, showed the same degree of accuracy.

When the specimen is brought into sharp focus (or to the degree of focus corresponding to the heat required), melting begins at the point where the surface of the material is subjected to direct heat. An increase in temperature above the melting point results in the lowering of the specimen's viscosity and surface tension after it has reached the molten stage. Single drops from the specimen gradually begin to appear in the crucible, followed shortly by a continuous flow.

Conn's series of experiments with the melting of silicates showed that considerable amounts of gases develop at the beginning of the melting process, but that these gases are released by the molten material itself. An intense boiling action was observed at the center of the sample, using a telescopic pyrometer.

Equilibrium between the incident radiant energy absorbed by the sample and the heat losses resulting from reradiation, heating of conduits, etc., occurred in about twenty minutes. At thermal equilibrium the intense reaction came to an end, whereupon the melt began to form as a pool of fine-grained liquid, free from bubbles and unmelted particles, at the bottom of the crucible. The diameter of this "crater" constantly increased as the heating continued.

In the melting of vitreous compounds, the crucible was moved back and forth from the focal point, causing it alternately to cool and resolidify, or to reheat and remelt. Repeated cooling and heating served to provide an approximate temperature series. The temperatures of the various melts of these vitreous or glassy compounds were then determined with great precision, on a spot measuring about 0.1 inch in diameter. Temperatures averaging 2273° F were recorded with a Model 8622C Leeds & Northrup optical pyrometer.

The crater on one of these tests was found to have a diameter of 0.235 inch close to the surface, and 0.2 inch further down to the bottom, where glass had been formed. This glass was perfectly clear, without either air bubbles or unmelted particles. Although some white glass was found at the orifice of the crater, most of the glass formed was a clear amber color.

Of considerable significance in this type of melting is the calculation of melt temperatures, based on the recorded value of 2273°F for the temperature of the crater itself. This crater temperature must first be converted to the absolute or Kelvin scale by changing it to centigrade (1245°C) and then adding 273, giving us 1518°K. We can then apply Wien's law as expressed by the formula

$$\frac{1}{T_4} = \frac{1}{1518} - \frac{0.650 \ln 0.0296}{14.380}$$

where T_4 is the actual melt temperature, 0.650 is the wavelength corresponding to the maximum effective transmission of the pyrometer filter measured in microns, the letters "ln" signifying logarithm to the base n; 0.0296 is the value of the sector transmission for the particular installation. The above equation then becomes

$$\frac{1}{T_4} = 0.0006588 - 0.0001592$$

$$T_4 = 2002° \text{ K} = 1729° \text{ C} = 3146° \text{ F}$$

which is the temperature of the melt.

Several samples were prepared of each substance listed in the table on page 81, and tested in the solar furnace by different observers at different times during the year. Samples containing up to 48 percent of clay yielded clear products on melting. Cooling in the air resulted in clear glass free from striae, due presumably to the great increase in crystallization of the melting products involved. In one particular test a temperature of 3679°F was reached in a 5-foot solar furnace, while in another test with a 10-foot reflector a reading of 3715°F was obtained.

The size of the solar image at the focal point was sufficiently small so that a crater with small diameter but considerable depth could be obtained. The crater was nevertheless large enough to permit observation of the melting and cooling of the material at the bottom. The diameter of the solar image depends, of course, on the focal length of the mirror. The maximum temperature obtainable for any given focal length depends, in turn on the diameter or aperture of the reflector. (This relationship is somewhat analogous to the f-number or stop setting on a camera lens; at the same focus, more or less light falls on the camera negative as the aperture is opened or closed.)

Extensive experience with Conn's solar furnaces has indicated that for a 5-foot reflector with a focal length of 26 inches, the diameter of the solar image is about ¼ inch, which is sufficient for most of the observations and tests on silicates. Actual observation of melting and cooling in silicate plants have frequently been more time-consuming than those in metallurgical research, because of the higher melting points of siliceous materials, which do not crystallize as readily at metals. Conn's experiments show that research in this field with the solar furnace offers many interesting opportunities for further study and opens up new areas of development for the silicate industry.

The 10-foot furnace constructed by Dr. Conn is now in operation at General Dynamics' Convair plant in San Diego, California, where the atmospheric conditions are more favorable for solar furnaces than in Kansas City. Conn has built a total of four solar furnaces, two of them with a diameter of 10 feet, made of ¼-inch aluminum sheet, two with smaller copper reflectors with 5-foot diameters.

On the matter of choosing between glass and metal for reflector surfaces, Dr. Conn merely points out the advantages and disadvantages of both. It is easier to build glass reflectors, which can be cast, molded, ground and polished a lot easier than metal reflectors; on the other hand, if molten material should fall on a glass reflector, the result would be disastrous, whereas a metal reflector would be only slightly damaged, depending on the material used; repolishing, of course, would be necessary. To repeat what was stated on page 73, the choice of reflector material involves three major factors, all of which are interrelated—cost, corrosion resistance, and percent reflectivity. Choice is therefore a matter of compromise in each particular application.

Extent of Solar Furnace Applications in the U.S. The impetus given to solar furnace construction in the United States by Dr. Conn is having ever-widening effect as the nation becomes more and more solar-energy conscious. As one example, sun-powered furnaces became available on a mass-product basis in 1957 with the release from surplus of hundreds of U.S. Army searchlights, which were sold or donated to colleges and universities for use in high-temperature research on ultrapure metals, jet and rocket compartments, and other strategic materials. These converted searchlights serve remarkably as solar furnaces, reaching temperatures up to 8000°F according to reliable reports. Materials to be studied are placed at the focal point of the searchlight, as in a regulation solar furnace, without danger of contamination by the walls as is the case when metals are heated to such elevated temperatures in refractory crucibles.

The Convair solar furnace, mentioned above, has been operated at temperatures as high as 8500°F, enough to melt a half-inch steel bolt in a matter of seconds. As modified by Convair, the furnace has an aluminum mirror with a diameter of 10 feet, and the material to be tested is held at the focal point of the parabolic surface by metal jaws. When in sharp focus the solar image is about the diameter of a five-cent piece. By way of comparison, an oxyacetylene torch develops temperatures of not more than 5000°F.

F. W. Fink, Convair's chief engineer at San Diego, says that the firm's research team soon discovered certain remarkable advantages of the solar furnace after it had been in operation a short while. One of these, previously referred to, is the fact that solar heat is ideal for research in high-purity metals or materials, since it eliminates impurities or foreign matter of all kinds. A second advantage is that no electric or magnetic fields are involved, as is the case with induction or other electric furnaces. Still another advantage is that no extraneous combustion gases are formed, as occurs in open-hearth or blast-furnace melting. In addition, the melting of samples can be observed accurately and without hazard, even at maximum temperatures, whereas all other types of furnaces are completely enclosed, with only a thick-walled glass observation slit through which to inspect the progress of the melt.

The Convair mirror has a 22-inch opening in its center, allowing unobstructed observation of the focal-point area from behind the mirror—a convenient, safe, and direct method that greatly enhances the research applications of the furnace. A synchronous motor, driving a precision clockwork mechanism, allows the reflector to follow the movement of the sun exactly, so that prolonged experiments lasting several hours are possible every day the sun shines. But because haze and clouds are the nemesis of all solar furnaces, regardless of how precise and efficient their design may be otherwise, the Convair people have decided to move their solar furnace from the industrialized San Diego area into the nearby Vallecito Mountains, where, for example, Cuyamaca Peak towers 6,500 feet—only 35 miles southeast of famed Mount Palomar, site of the world's largest telescope. In the untroubled air of these mountain ranges the solar furnace should operate at its highest peak of efficiency.

Until 1958 the Convair furnace was the largest of its kind in the United States, but in that year it lost the title to the new solar furnace built by the United States Army at Natick, Massachusetts, about 15 miles southwest of Boston. According to an Army press release, the new furnace, which began operating on September 30, 1958, would be able to "intensify ordinary sunshine into temperatures approaching those generated by a nuclear blast." Designed for laboratory testing of materials intended to protect military personnel against the high-temperature effects of atomic weapons, the Natick solar furnace was expected to produce temperatures in the range of 10,000°F. After one month of operation, scientists were able to cut through solid I-beams of the type used for bridges and heavy construction "as easily as one chars paper with a common magnifying glass." Army officials indicated that the furnace would be used to study the effects of high temperature on building materials and lubricants. The Natick solar furnace collects and focuses about five times as much solar energy as the Convair model described above, and is of more advanced design.

Trombe's Work with Solar Furnaces. We have already noted (page 44) the achievements of French scientists in the field of solar energy. The Fifth Republic carries on in the great tradition of Lavoisier, Cassini, and de Saussure, contributing a generous share of inventions in solar application despite the fact that today the funds available for French scientific research are only a fifth of the amount at the disposal of their British and American colleagues. To mention a few French inventions in other than solar energy fields we may note the Montgolfiers (balloons), Levassor (gasoline engine and motor car), Benedictus (laminated glass), Claude (neon lamps), Lumière (motion pictures), Robert (papermaking machine), Niepce (photography), Herroult (electric steel), Coufignale (adding machine), and Dupouy (electron microscope). To list some of the French achievements in pure science would perhaps fill the rest of this chapter.

One of the most striking manifestations of French inventiveness and ingenuity is the solar melting installation designed and built by Dr. Félix Trombe at Mont Louis in the French Pyrénées. Long a serious student of Straubel's work in solar energy (page 78), Trombe in 1946 began his own research at Meudon near Paris, aided by funds from the Centre Nationale de la Recherche Scientifique. From the start he was convinced that solar furnaces had enormous possibilities for high-temperature research work, and that observed efficiencies of over 50 percent at temperatures as high as 5400°F proved them superior to conventional furnaces.

The equipment he first used at Meudon consisted of converted German antiaircraft searchlights and parabolic sound collectors used in wartime for detection of enemy aircraft engines. The average diameter of these reflectors was about 6 feet, with focal distances of 30 to 35 inches. As the U.S. Army was to discover in its turn, such A.A. searchlight collectors can make rather efficient solar furnaces (page 84).

Trombe made only minor modifications to the searchlight housings and mounts, using the two axes of the latter to orient the optical axis of the mirror in the direction of the sun, and adding an auxiliary mirror at this optical axis, parallel to that of the mirror. A lens having a focal length of 4 feet was used to project the sun's image on a screen consisting of 3,000 plates in trapeziform arrangement fastened by 12,000 screws.

The original reflecting mirrors of the searchlights were silver-planted, and only a sixteenth of an inch in thickness. At high temperatures they were subject to distortion and cracking. Trombe replaced these with more efficient reflectors made of anodized aluminum, shaped to the proper convexity by spinning, and later highly polished. Before deciding on the aluminum, however, Trombe had made numerous experiments with heat-resistant or tempered glass mirrors, but their extra thickness, complicated by the problem of double refraction, eliminated them from further consideration. However, when Trombe began in 1947 to experiment with aluminum-coated heat-resistant glass reflectors, he found that the combination provided a better corrosion resistance than the anodized aluminum alone, so that a compromise between the two types of reflectors was reached, paralleling somewhat the experience of Conn in the United States (page 81). (The aluminum coating seems to have solved the problem of double refraction, and everyone knows the high resistance that glass has to corrosion and weathering.)

Among other materials tested in Trombe's solar furnace was graphite, which combines with oxygen in the air at temperatures above 1100°F, although, as physicists know, it can be heated as high as 5400°F in inert atmospheres without melting or undergoing chemical change. In the solar furnace, exposed as it is to atmospheric air, the graphite forms oxidation products that are spattered around the edges of the furnace in the form of crystals.

Quartz, the commonest form of silica (SiO_2) is the principal ingredient of heat-resistant glass, because of its very high melting point, which is in the neighborhood of 3100°F—a property that also makes it a valuable material for crucibles and for tubes and rods in conventional furnaces. One would expect, therefore, that even in the solar furnace quartz is pretty difficult to melt. Quartz sand, a translucent form of quartz, resists melting up to about

2000°F, although it devitrifies at 1920°F, and fused silica of the same chemical content devitrifies at about 1100°F and shatters when suddenly cooled. Trombe succeeded in melting quartz sand having a grain size of from 0.020 to 0.040 inch.

Thorium, another high-melting-point material, is a rare metal mostly known to the layman in the form of thorium nitrate (incandescent gas mantles) or in other compounds used in luminous paints and flashlight powders. It has a melting point of about 3090°F. Trombe was able to melt this rare metal within about a minute after bringing the sun's rays to a sharp focus. It does not volatilize during the melting process, and it acquires a marked degree of transparency upon cooling after being subjected to the solar-furnace "treatment."

Zirconium, with an even higher melting point than thorium (3360°F), also yielded to Trombe's solar furnace in about one minute, which represents a considerable advance over the results of Dr. Conn (page 80), who, in addition to requiring a longer "warm-up" time, produced an uneven melt with particles of undissolved metal. Zirconium did not exhibit any amount of transparency after solar fusion and subsequent cooling.

Magnesium powder, the kind used for pyrotechnical and flash-bulb uses, is made by shaving metallic magnesium (melting point 1100°F) into fine curly threads to provide maximum surface area per weight. When placed in the solar furnace it melts almost instantaneously, with a highly actinic flare, but oddly enough this is only a surface melting. Lime (calcium oxide, CaO), which lent its name to "limelight," has a very high melting point—4660°F. Used as a flux in blast-furnace operations, lime itself melts rather readily in the solar furnace, the melt turning yellow due to the traces of iron oxide and other impurities generally present unless purified beforehand in a furnace or kiln.

Titanium oxide (melting point 3317°F) also melted easily enough in Trombe's solar device, but turned black after doing so, probably because of the presence of Ilmenite ore, a black ore of titanium. Another titanium ore, rutile, is red; by way of contrast, titanium oxide, an important ingredient of paints, is a pure white. The study of these compounds while they are actually being melted may help further to explain these and other fascinating aspects of their physical and chemical properties.

Chromium, once a rare metal but now the bane of every car owner's existence, with a melting point of 2750°F, melted in less than a minute in the Trombe furnace, but molybdenum, which has a melting point of 4750°F, is extremely difficult to melt in *any* furnace, because above 1400°F the metal forms an oxide which volatalizes or evaporates as it forms, so that one winds up with close to nothing in the crucible instead of a molten mass. (Of course this applies only to atmospheric furnaces; under proper conditions of pressure and temperature, molybdenum can be turned to liquid like any other metal.)

In 1952 Dr. Trombe received the necessary funds for the erection of a solar furnace at Fort Mont Louis, a fortification built by a renowned French military engineer, the Marquis Sebastien de Vauban, in 1690. Here, in these historic surroundings high in the French Pyrénées, Trombe set about the construction of a really enormous installation that dwarfed the very largest solar furnaces built up to that time.

With the aid of dozens of trained workmen Trombe devised a "wall" of mirrors consisting of no less than 168 separate plane mirrors of silvered glass, each 20 by 20 inches in size and ⅛ inch thick. In front of this mirror wall, he erected a second mirror which was even larger—a concave reflector 35 feet in diameter made up of 3,500 individual elements, situated a full 70 feet from the first mirror. The wall of 168 plane mirrors has an ingenious mount and orienting device that moves it automatically to follow the sun from sunrise to sunset. This, together with the fact that sunshine is quite abundant in southern France, means that the massive solar furnace can be effectively operated up to 10 hours daily during 250 days of the year, including the vagaries of the weather and the unpredictability of cloud formation. So far the maximum temperatures reported have been of the order of 5400°F, with an average working temperature of about 4900°F. With such temperatures, 40 to 60 pounds of quartz or 130 pounds of iron can be easily melted in an hour. Subsequent improvements are said to have increased these capacities to 200–400 pounds per hour.

Installations like these are of extraordinary scientific value in the study of ceramic materials, silicates, nitrides, carbides, borides, and other refractory-hard materials. The complete absence of contaminating electrodes and refractory walls, plus the high-intensity, short-duration character of the heating, makes the solar furnace one of the most valuable tools of present-day scientific research. And as the new edition of this book goes to press there is word that Professor Trombe is working on the construction of a 131-foot solar furnace that will develop 1,000 kilowatts of power at the focus—compared with 70 kw developed by the present Mont Louis furnace!

SOLAR MOTORS

Solar motors, not to be confused with solar furnaces or solar cookers, are a very specialized class of machines, unknown to the fathers of the Industrial Revolution. They convert solar energy into a power source for driving pumps, steam engines and other mechanical devices—directly, without the use of conventional or nuclear fuels.

We have already mentioned Captain John Ericsson's solar motor of 1868 (page 46), which used an 18-foot reflector and a 6-inch tubular boiler, developing up to 4 horsepower continuously when the sun was out. The next important development in solar motors—also American—took place in 1901, when Frank Shuman built his huge solar motor at Pasadena, California, using a mirror with a diameter twice that of Ericsson's.

This huge reflector—it measured 36 feet 6 inches across the widest end, and tapered to 15 feet at the bottom—consisted of no fewer than 1,788 individual plane mirrors arranged in the form of an inverted umbrella, which focused the sun's rays on a fire-tube boiler mounted over it. The mounting of the mirror was such that, with the aid of clockwork, it could be kept constantly turned toward the sun. The boiler held 100 gallons of water, with space for 8 cubic feet of steam. In operation, this remarkable device is said to have had an output of 10 horsepower and to have driven a steam engine connected to a load.

Emboldened by his success, Shuman built a second solar motor in 1908 at Tacony, a suburb of Philadelphia. It consisted of a "collector" rather than a reflector, a low-pressure steam engine, a steam condenser, and various auxiliary motors. The entire collector was placed at the bottom of a large wooden box covered, greenhouse fashion, by two glass plates. Between the two plates was a dead-air space of about one inch. The pipes that comprised the collector were blackened on the outside, and the bottom of the box itself was likewise protected against heat loss by a 2-inch-thick cork lining. All of the parts were mounted on frames that could be raised on one side up to 30 inches from the ground, so that the operator could observe from time to time the effect of the sun.

In addition to the collector, Shuman employed two plane mirrors whose function was to deflect the solar rays onto the glass plates. These were not focusing mirrors, but merely deflectors that made possible the horizontal installation of the collector—which otherwise would have had to be angled continuously to follow the sun's motion.

Inside the collector pipes Shuman placed a heat-transfer medium—ordinary ether, the volatile liquid used in medicine as an anesthetic. This was long before the days of ethylene glycol, the modern antifreeze so widely used today for heat-exchange applications.

Shuman was evidently well acquainted with the mechanics and thermodynamics of steam plant operation. Besides using condensers which converted the exhausted steam back into feedwater, he went so far as to install steam traps as well, which drained off condensed steam in supply lines and other parts of the system, thereby increasing his efficiency still further. The steam drum, which supplied the low-pressure reciprocating steam engine, had a diameter of 16 inches—about the size of a domestic hot-water tank.

This well-designed solar power installation developed a maximum output of 32 horsepower; its average daily output over an eight-hour period was 14 horsepower. It operated a reciprocating pump that could move water at the rate of 3,600 gallons per minute at about 13 pounds per square inch pressure (30-foot head). The water was used for irrigation purposes.

By 1913 Shuman was ready for even bigger and better solar power plants. With the assistance of his consultant engineer, Sir Charles V. Boys of London, he erected a new plant in Meadi, near Cairo, Egypt. Although based on the same general principle as the two earlier plants—and intended, as before, to supply power for irrigation—the new plant was not only of larger capacity than the first two combined but also eliminated a heat-transfer fluid by directing the sun's rays onto the steam generator itself instead of using a collector.

Shuman actually used not one but 572 steam generators in this imposing installation, 22 sets being arranged in 26 rows. Each generator or boiler had its own individual mirror, which rotated about its horizontal axis so as to keep the rays of the sun reflected onto the boiler drum to which it was connected. The entire layout occupied 43,752 square feet of ground area, or roughly about a third of an acre. All the boilers were connected in parallel to both the feedwater line and the steam-collecting header, which in turn was connected, with proper valves and manifolding, to a reciprocating steam pump. Steam pressure built up to 22 pounds per square inch, and the developed horsepower applied at the pump piston was calculated at 50 hp over a ten-hour day. This was a pretty substantial installation, even for a conventionally fired boiler; the total efficiency of the system, if input energy on a cost-per-pound-of-fuel basis were to be somehow worked into the equation, would be extremely high, since there were no fuel costs whatever.

Remshardt's Analysis. In a detailed review* of Shuman's solar power plant installations, the German physicist Adolf Remshardt of Stuttgart begins by stating that there are two possible ways of converting solar radiation into mechanical power with the intermediate use of the steam cycle. These two methods have to do only with the actual utilization of the sun's rays as a fuel or prime mover. According to Remshardt, you must either concentrate the rays by means of a convex or parabolic mirror—or with some system of lenses (which have not proved as efficient as reflectors), or else you must allow the sun's rays to fall directly on the area to be heated. Simple and obvious as that may sound, it is a scientific fact that must be realized before any design work can proceed. Remshardt then goes on to say that in his opinion the "concentrated" method appeared to be the more practical if moderately high steam pressure (which in the 1920s meant about 250 psi) combined with reasonably good efficiency, were to be attained. Shuman, he noted, used a concentration ratio of only 4.5 to 1, which in his estimation was far too low—one reason, no doubt, why the American inventor's resulting steam pressure was only a little higher than atmospheric.

Proceeding with his analysis, Remshardt gives a few additional reasons why optical lenses, rather than reflecting mirrors, have proved inefficient for concentrating the sun's rays in solar engines. The major objections to lenses are twofold: they are (1) too heavy, and (2) too expensive. Metal reflectors or mirrors are to be preferred, not only over lenses but over glass mirrors also.

When the reflector is not adjusted with great precision—either

* *Proceedings of the Association of German Engineers,* 1926, p. 529.

in the focusing or in the angle it makes with the sun—then the overall efficiency of the solar plant falls off, because only a part of the designed amount of solar "fuel" is then being used, thus increasing the ratio of heat losses to input. Conic mirrors have some advantages in that they are easier to keep in adjustment, but they do not lend themselves readily to a multiple arrangement of the kind used by Shuman.

Remshardt's recommendations point to the use of a metal reflector in the shape of a paraboloid of revolution, which he claimed could be easily manufactured with sufficient precision for most applications. The reflector (or mirror—the terms are used interchangeably) must be mounted so as to follow the sun, meaning that it should have two axes of rotation, at right angles to each other, as mentioned earlier in this book (page 74). According to the Stuttgart engineer, the simultaneous movement of a battery of reflectors such as used by Shuman at Cairo has to be accomplished as smoothly as possible. It will help, therefore, to have their axes pass through their centers of gravity so that their motion is balanced in all positions or angles.

In his summary, Remshardt reiterates the two cardinal principles of solar power design: (1) a solar engine must be able to convert the sun's heat into mechanical power with a minimum of losses in every element of the design, and (2) it must be so designed as to permit continuous adjustment to changing meteorological conditions, fluctuations of solar radiation intensities, and the daily and seasonal movements of the sun.

Schultz's Sulfur Dioxide Motor. An ingenious solar motor was constructed by the German inventor Robert Schultz of Dirschau (formerly part of Prussia) as early as 1881. Instead of water, Schultz used sulfur dioxide as the heat-transfer medium—the same colorless gas (SO_2), also known as sulfurous acid anhydride, that is used extensively today in domestic refrigerators. It has a condensing pressure of 51.7 pounds per square inch at 86°F, and a vaporization pressure of 2.9 psi at 5°F. It is liquid at 14°F, and boils at about the same temperature. At 95°F it develops a pressure of approximately 5 atmospheres, and correspondingly higher pressures as the temperature is increased. Schultz conducted the sulfur dioxide vapors produced by direct solar heating into a steam engine, where they gave up their heat, which in turn was converted into mechanical power. He used a closed cycle, condensing the sulfur dioxide vapor and recirculating the liquid as in the modern gas refrigerator.

Krenn's Mercury Motor. The first continuous-acting solar motor was developed by an Austrian engineer named Krenn in the late 1890s. Continuous-acting, of course, implies that it ran day or night, rain or shine. Since Krenn's claim has enormous implications for the future of solar energy, it will be worthwhile to examine his apparatus in some detail.

It was, to be sure, as complicated in its arrangement as it was original in its design and construction. No duplicate of this plant was ever attempted by anyone since—perhaps because of its very complexity.* But its avowed principle of continuous action, whether or not attained in practice, should be of sufficient interest to stimulate others along similar lines, improving or simplifying the original design where possible.

Krenn was highly original in his choice of a heat-transfer fluid. We have seen how Shuman used ether, and Schultz sulfur dioxide for this purpose; both Marcuse of Germany and Abbot of the United States employed oil with a high boiling point. Mercury probably appealed to Krenn because of its even higher boiling point—622°F.

Krenn used three parabolic mirrors in his device, each of which was equipped with a coil of pipe at its focal point, serving the function of an evaporator. A feed pump transported the mercury from the boiler into the uppermost of three tandem evaporators, and from thence into the other two evaporators below. The heat of solar radiation concentrated by the mirrors at the focal point vaporized the mercury in the evaporators, the mercury vapor being then carried to the mercury turbine by way of a flexible tube. On entering the mercury turbine the mercury vapor had a temperature of about 734°F and a pressure of about 14 psi, or one atmosphere; at the exhaust end of the mercury turbine, the mercury vapor was exhausted into the shell of a mercury condenser containing tubes through which water circulated. At this stage the mercury vapor still has a high temperature—approximately 450°F at about one atmosphere, enough to boil the water in the condenser tubes, and the steam produced in this manner was conducted to a steam turbine, which converted it to mechanical power. This combined use of mercury vapor and water vapor

* But see report of space application below, page 111.

is known to power engineers as the "binary-fluid cycle," and while its use is not widespread in conventional power stations, a few notable installations are in operation today. One of these is at the South Meadow Station of the Hartford Electric Light Company, where mercury vapor drives a 15,000-kilowatt mercury turbine, then generates steam in two condensers to drive a 20,000-kilowatt steam turbine. This binary-fluid installation uses 136,000 pounds of liquid mercury circulating through 668 steel tubes.

Thus Krenn's arrangement produced mechanical power from solar energy from two separate sources—a mercury turbine, operated by mercury vapor produced by solar heat, and a steam turbine, operated by steam produced from water by the residual heat of the mercury vapor after it had been used to drive the mercury turbine.

How did Krenn's apparatus act as a "continuous" solar power plant day and night, rain or shine? The answer to this is a matter of interpretation of what a solar power plant is. Krenn's extant drawings clearly show that he used coal or coke to preheat the mercury liquid before it was vaporized in the "evaporators" placed at the solar foci of the three reflectors. Accordingly, it was not a "pure" solar power plant, which in our definition is one that uses no fuel whatever other than incident sunlight. Secondly, the heat that was eventually transferred from the exhausted mercury vapor to the feedwater in the condenser tubes to convert the water into steam had a great many Btu's "borrowed" from the coal or coke used in the furnace, and how much the solar reflectors added to this is questionable. Third, if the plant ran at night and on cloudy days, it probably was only the steam turbine that was operating, using a head of steam that had already been developed the previous day or two. The solar reflectors, by giving an added "push" to the process of vaporizing the mercury, unquestionably added to the overall efficiency of the plant, but for the foregoing reasons it cannot be considered a "continuous acting" solar power plant, nor even a 100 percent solar power plant.

Solar Motors of the Sixties. Coming now to present-day solar motor projects, we should perhaps mention India first of all, because the mass production of small solar motors, costing about $20 each, is being planned there. These motors are intended for use in households, and are to work on the principle of plane solar mirrors. The design calls for a total reflecting surface of 150 square feet, which will produce the same amount of solar power as a parabolic reflector with a diameter of 7.8 feet.

Algeria also is turning to utilization of solar energy, because of its precarious power supply. Its population of 10 million consumes about a billion kilowatts of electric power, yet the only available coal deposits are small—not more than 300,000 tons annually—and are located deep in the interior of the continent, about 370 miles from the coast. Existing hydroelectric power plants produce only 330 million kilowatts, and that only under favorable hydrological conditions.

In cooperation with the French Supreme Council for Scientific Research, the Sautter-Harlé Company of Paris has erected a solar reflector in the vicinity of the Bouzaréah observatory near Algiers. This experimental model, designed for research purposes, has an outer diameter of 27 feet, an inner diameter of 6 feet, and a radiation surface of 590 square feet. Present plans call for the construction of a larger number of reflectors in the near future.

On clear days, the design capacity of the Bouzaréah reflector is said to be 50 kilowatts, and clear days in North Africa are not rare by any means—in fact, solar radiation there is of great intensity at least 3,000 hours out of every year. Anodized aluminum, suitably formed and polished, has been chosen as the material for this reflector. A thin layer of plastic will also be added to the reflecting surface to increase corrosion resistance. Total reflective power of this combination is said to be 82 percent. However, the problem of converting solar power into mechanical power has not been completely solved in this North African installation.

LARGE-SCALE SOLAR POWER PLANTS

In 1958 the Soviet Union's eminent physicist, Dr. V. A. Baum (page 55), head of the Solar Technical Laboratories in Tashkent, Turkestan, revealed that work had been proceeding since 1955 on the construction of an enormous solar power plant in the scorching hot plain of Ararat, near the Turkish border. The purpose of this plant is to supply steam for heating and processing, on a scale sufficient for a town of 20,000 persons; some of this steam will be used to generate electricity as well.

To visualize this "space age" solar installation as described by Dr. Baum, imagine a revolving, cylindrical steam boiler in the shape of a gigantic water tower 12 stories high (131 feet, actually). With this as a center, place twenty-three concentric, circular railway tracks around it, and on each track set a locomotive with a string of flatcars behind it. On these flatcars, place a total of 1,293 plane mirrors, each 10 feet high by 16 feet long. Equip each of these mirrors with automatic tilting devices, electric control motors, photoelectric cells and magnetic amplifiers, and then give the signal to start all 23 trains moving around the tower.

This, truly, is solar heating on a colossal scale, but it is only half the picture. The Power Research Institute of the Soviet Academy of Sciences has announced that it has designed and built solar mirror systems capable of amplifying the incident energy of the sun's rays from 25 to *10,000 times*. Light amplification by means of "lasers" has been an accomplished fact in the United States since 1960, these devices, like the better-known "masers" (*m*olecular *a*mplification by *s*timulated *e*mission of *r*adiation) being *paramagnetic amplifiers* which emit controllable electromagnetic energy when stimulated by a low-power signal. Whether the Russians are planning to use lasers in Ararat is not known at the present writing, but no doubt some form of solar amplification will be used.

The heat-transfer surface of the central boiler is a 26-foot by 50-foot flat screen made up of a network of pipes. The combined reflecting surface of the 1,293 mirrors at 160 square feet each is 208,000 square feet. Researches conducted by Soviet scientists showed that each square foot of the ground surface in the Ararat valley receives about 700,000 Btu of solar radiation in the course of a year, and that in the same period 2,600 hours of sunshine can be expected. Basing their calculations on these and other factors, the designers estimate that the capacity of the plant will be about 2½ million kilowatts per year.

Besides local heating and lighting, the output of this huge solar power plant is intended to benefit the agriculture of the Armenian Republic by supplying low-cost power for irrigation and drainage. One interesting feature of the overall design is the fact that the entire area will be planted with a dense ground cover to eliminate the dust problem, which would otherwise seriously reduce the reflecting power of the 1,293 mirrors.

Solar vs. Other Types of Power. A necessary step in the designing of large solar power plants is to compare their estimated total costs with those of conventional and atomic power plants of comparable output. A solar power plant using either plane mirrors or parabolic metal reflectors naturally requires a larger ground area than an atomic power plant of the same capacity. Atomic or nuclear power plants are certainly the most compact of all in terms of volume of fuel required; the energy released in the complete fission of a pound of uranium 235 is roughly equivalent to that produced by the complete combustion of a thousand tons of coal.

A solar power plant of 100,000 kilowatt capacity requires a radiation surface (assuming chromium mirrors) of about three-tenths of a square mile, or roughly a million square yards, which is about 215 acres—two-thirds the size of the Republic of Monaco, for example, or the area of Central Park in New York City from the Plaza Hotel to the Metropolitan Museum of Art. This is admittedly a lot of space to fill with mirrors. It helps somewhat to substitute pure aluminum for the chromium, reducing the acreage needed to around 130, or something like 600,000 square yards. An atomic power plant of the same capacity (the closest one in size now in operation is the 80,000-kw Shippingport plant of the Duquesne Light Company near Pittsburgh, Pa.) would take up about one acre, more or less. To generate the same amount of power, the atomic power plant needs only 390 pounds of uranium 235; the Shippingport reactor, in operation since 1957, uses about 9 tons of U-235 a year to supply 300,000 families with light and power.

In the localities that we have been considering—the valley of Ararat, the Sahara, and other unpopulated areas, the vast areas of ground surface needed for solar energy plants represent only a minor difficulty, but the cost and upkeep of thousands of mirrors is a little more costly, as well as the installation and upkeep of thousands of feet of piping. On the other hand, the "fuel" for solar power plants does not have to be replaced from year to year, as in an atomic power or conventional plant; in ten years, let us say, the Shippingport plant will have bought and consumed 90 tons or 18,000 pounds of U-235 (and disposed of the radioactive wastes) while our theoretical solar power plant will have had to purchase no fuel whatever, assuming the sun keeps shining as predicted. And of course the maintenance costs of the two are vastly different—replacement and polishing of mirrors, etc., vs. complete shutdown and decontamination for two months or so every eighteen months, during which all equipment, machines, piping, gauges, and meters must be checked and replaced if defective or unsafe, as required by the U.S. Atomic Energy Commission.

Where 200 acres or similar large tracts are not available for solar power plants, solar energy can be harnessed and converted to electrical energy by means of photoelectric cells and solar batteries, as we shall see below. At the present time such applications are limited to small devices, like satellite transmitters and receivers, solar hearing aids, and solar clocks, but these devices work with a high degree of efficiency. Silicon cells, which serve as their basic working principle, are expensive now, but so was aluminum before Charles Hall made possible the mass production of this versatile metal. With common sand as one of the principal ingredients of silicates, perhaps in the not too distant future we will be using it to convert solar energy into mechanical power on a much larger scale.

SOLAR ENERGY IN THE SPACE AGE

Sun-Operated Telephones. One of the major inventions of the year 1954 was the solar battery developed by scientists of the Bell Telephone Laboratories in Murray Hill, New Jersey, about 12 miles from Newark. The conversion of light energy to electricity is not new, having been discovered accidentally in 1873 by a telegraph engineer named Joseph May, who was working on resistance measurements at the Valencia, Ireland end of the Atlantic cable. He was using selenium resistors, which caused his measurements to fluctuate wildly whenever the sun shone on them directly. The American inventor G. R. Carey in 1875 built a special camera modeled after the human eye, using a bank of selenium cells to duplicate the human retina. And in 1887 the German "father of radio," Heinrich Hertz, performed numerous experiments with selenium and other photoelectric cells, but actually it was not until the development of sound motion pictures that the photoelectric cell received much attention.

Bell Lab's solar battery, therefore, represents the culmination of a long development from the feeble currents produced by early selenium cells to a miniaturized "power pack" strong enough to operate telephone circuits, short- and long-wave transmitters and receivers, and even television transmitters far out in space.

The Bell solar battery consists of a large disk made up of 432 smaller disks of very thin silicon sheets, each of these having an area of about one square inch. These cells, sealed in plastic and covered with glass, were enclosed in an aluminum casing measuring 2 feet by 3 feet. The silicon used, though highly purified, is extracted from ordinary sand.

Silicon is a "semiconductor" used in the manufacture of transistors, which were invented by three Bell Telephone engineers in 1948—William Shockley, John Bardeen, and Walter Brattain. When light strikes a semiconductor, it causes a rupture of the electronic bond structure in the crystal lattice, leaving a defect or "hole," which may be filled immediately by another electron, causing the "hole" to appear to move throughout the bond structure. Transistors depend for their operation on either an excess of "free" electrons or a deficit of electrons (excess of holes) in covalent bonds; a semiconductor having an excess of free electrons is called an n-type, whereas one with an excess of "holes" is called a p-type. It so happens that n and p also imply "negative" and "positive" respectively; the n-type does have an excess of negative carriers, and the p-type an excess of positive carriers. An excess of either is produced by first refining the semiconductor to an extraordinary degree of purity, then adding minute amounts of "impurities" in the form of either phosphorus, arsenic, antimony or bismuth, which produce n-type silicon (or germanium); or boron, aluminum, gallium or thorium, which produce p-type silicon (or germanium). Antimony and arsenic are generally used as "donor" elements or impurities to create n-type silicon; aluminum and gallium are typical "acceptors" that create p-type silicon. A transistor essentially consists of a combination of two p-n junctions (arranged as p-n-p or n-p-n), and, through a series of electronic changes too complex to describe here, it is then capable of performing many of the functions of electron tubes, including amplification and control of radio-frequency currents. (R. S. Ohe and J. H. Scaff discovered the principle of p-n compounds in 1930, but did not apply it to the development of what later became the transistor.)

The light that strikes the solar battery sets up a steady migration of holes and electrons within the silicon crystals, varying directly with the intensity of the sunlight. The tiny currents from

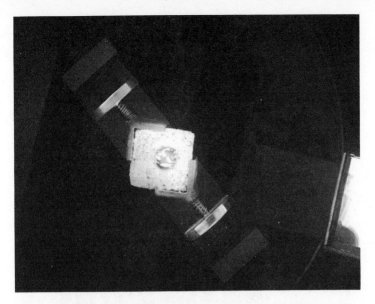

Photograph of ceramic sample as hole is being burned in it by the sun's rays, concentrated by the Convair solar furnace at San Diego. (*General Dynamics Corp.*)

Bell Telephone Company's solar battery, shown here being installed on top of a telephone pole, uses energy from the sun's rays to operate the world's first "sun telephone" line at Americus, Georgia. Thin silicon cells convert the sun's energy directly into electricity.

Bell Laboratories engineer holding 9-cell element of telephone solar battery; 48 of these make up total of 432 silicon cells. (*Bell Telephone Laboratories.*)

each silicon "cell" are connected in series so that they are additive; a number of such batteries may then be connected either in series, parallel, or series-parallel, depending on the total current, voltage and capacity desired, just as with ordinary dry cells. One big difference, however, is that since the solar is always generating in the sunlight, its current would be wasted if it were not connected to storage batteries, which conveniently store the solar energy in the form of current potential for use at night or in bad weather.

The first long-distance telephone call made with the Bell solar battery took place on October 4, 1955, over a telephone line serving eight farmhouses near Americus, Georgia. The battery was mounted on top of one of the telephone poles located in the experimental area. Since the daily solar radiation during October is much less than that of summer, as much current as possible had to be produced for storage within a few hours. To achieve this, the solar battery plate with its silicon cells was mounted so that its surface faced south at a 60-degree angle to the horizon, in accordance with prior calculations by Bell Laboratories engineers.

The original solar batteries operated at about 6 percent efficiency, the same as a modern gasoline engine. Improvements since 1955 have increased their efficiency to about 11 percent, which is half of the theoretical maximum of 22 percent. During the hours of bright sunlight a single unit can produce about 10 watts of electric power—enough to supply a small telephone installation and to charge storage batteries as well. Thus a few hours of sunshine during each day are sufficient to maintain trouble-free telephone operation without the use of the conventional line current from central exchanges.

At first glance it might appear that the solar battery, ingenious though it may be, is not likely to be an important source of power, or represent a significant saving, to a large public utility like a phone company. The average rural telephone circuit operates on about one watt of power—roughly 20 volts at 50 milliamperes. Whether the current comes from solar batteries on poles or chemical batteries in the telephone exchange, the same amount of wiring and equipment has to be used. Where, then, is the big saving—and why would Bell Laboratories spend a great deal of time and money developing solar batteries when ordinary dry or wet chemical batteries would be "just as good"?

The answer is that the solar battery is not only more efficient than chemical batteries, but it has a practically indefinite life, with no parts to wear out, no fluids to replace, no plates to be renewed, no "input" but the sun itself. Silicon cells never lose their capability of converting sunlight into electric current, whereas every other type of battery known to science or industry will eventually wear out, even if it is not used. Chemical batteries can be recharged, but this consumes current; solar batteries never need recharging, and have an infinite "shelf life." One can begin to see the savings accrue in two, five or ten years, especially when a large number of chemical batteries can be replaced with solar batteries. If this were not sufficient reason for costly research and development by Bell Laboratories and other companies, consider the vast and as yet untapped applications of the solar battery in the space age—communication satellites, manned satellites, manned space platforms, lunar exploration, and, eventually, interplanetary rocket ships. As we shall see a bit farther on, the solar battery is an indispensable feature of all these devices or projects, some of which are already actualities, such as the day-long orbital flights of Gherman Titov and Gordon Cooper.

SOLAR-POWERED RADIO AND TV TRANSMITTERS

In 1954, the same year that Bell announced its solar battery, the General Electric Company at its electronics plant in Syracuse, N.Y., put solar energy to work experimentally as power for a radio transmitter. Considerably improved in the years since then, the original model was about the size of a package of king-size cigarettes. What had made this miniature size possible was the coincidental development of transistors, which were just coming into fairly wide use at the time, although the era of subminiaturization and microminiaturization was still ahead in the sixties. The solar-energy cells used were selenium, as described above on page 99; germanium was also used in later adaptations.

While the solar-operated transmitter did not have immediate application for the man on the street, two important developments did take place, partly as a result of this invention and the research behind it. One of these was the phenomenal growth in the number of miniaturized transistor radios, not much bigger than a pack of cigarettes, which one sees on (or in) every hand, especially during baseball season, followed not long after by the development of

Transistorized radio transmitter powered by solar cells. (*General Electric Company.*)

Patek Philippe "Pendulette" clock run by solar energy. When either natural or artificial light falls on the solar cells located in the cover, an electric current is generated that charges a small accumulator or storage cell. A sufficient charge keeps it running for as long as a year. (*Patek Philippe, Geneva.*)

Left, a solar-powered flashlight in which the solar cells shown on the handle charge a nickel-cadmium battery which supplies electrical energy to light the bulb all night long. Right, the world's first sun-powered radio-phonograph, developed by the Admiral Corporation of New York. It is powered by a 48-cell solar battery that operates on artificial light as well as sunlight. Standby batteries provide current if there is no light at all available.

Top, the "Solarion," a sun-powered clock perfected by General Time Corporation and produced by its Seth Thomas Division. The clock has three major parts—the solar energy converters, an electrical accumulator for energy storage during periods of darkness, and the clock mechanism itself. Ten solar cells and sufficient sunlight or incandescent light are enough to keep it running indefinitely. Bottom, the solar-powered highway flasher, which provides continuous operation at night by means of solar cells and electrical accumulator. The flasher will operate all night long to warn motorists of obstructions up ahead.

two-way transistorized "citizen's band" walkie-talkies, with ranges up to ten or more miles on simple dry-cell batteries that need only infrequent replacement because of the low drain of the transistorized circuitry. The second development, more directly connected with solar power, was the wider use of solar-operated transmitters in the U.S. Government's space satellite program, beginning with the long-heralded *Vanguard I,* launched March 17, 1958, which carried silicon solar batteries *and is still transmitting as of this writing.* (Satellites and space vehicles are considered in greater detail on pages 133–147 below.)

Solar Hearing Aids. Closely allied to solar transmitters is the manufacture, by Zenith Radio Corporation and others, of hearing aids powered by tiny solar batteries employing silicon cells. First announced in July of 1958, by Zenith, the hearing devices are even smaller than their predecessors, being disguised in an ordinary pair of shell-rimmed eyeglasses. The silicon cells produce more than enough current to amplify conversations and music for the hard-of-hearing. What makes them thoroughly practical is the fact that the selenium cells are activated by normal amounts of electric and other artificial light, so that the wearer is not obliged to stand in the sun in order to hear what is going on. The cells charge a miniaturized storage battery in the other of the two eyepieces. Even the diffused sunlight received on an ordinary overcast day is sufficient to operate the cells so that the storage battery is not drained, and on such days "recharging" can be effected merely by standing or sitting under a 100-watt lamp!

Clocks Run by the Sun. Two long-established watchmaking companies, continents apart, brought out simultaneously in 1957 their own separate versions of solar-powered clocks—General Time Corporation of New York and Patek Philippe of Geneva. General Time's model was described as being "completely portable," and contained a series of silicon cells that charge an "accumulator cell" when exposed to sunlight. The accumulator in turn provides the tiny current needed to run the clock. According to the manufacturer, one day's exposure to light will run the clock for a month, without any further exposure. A sufficiently long exposure will keep the clock operating for a year or more without any light whatever.

Patek Phillipe's "Pendulette" is also based on the photoelectric-cell principle, and is said to operate on artificial light as well as on sunlight. Although highly sensitive to small amounts of light, it can also withstand prolonged exposure to strong sunshine. It, too, uses an accumulator, and the same kind of claim is made for the Pendulette—i.e., that a sufficient solar "charge" will keep it running for a year or so. The tiny motor built by Patek Philippe for the Pendulette is of especially ingenious construction, utilizing a collector with three gold disks and conductor wires of precious-metal alloy. With 28 sapphire jeweled bearings, the clock is almost frictionless, so that current of only a few microamperes is sufficient to set the gear train in motion and keep it running with a very high degree of accuracy. If exposed to as little as 19 foot-candles of light for four hours a day the stored energy in the accumulator does not have to be used.

New Art—Helioglyphics? "The Moving Finger writes;" said Edward FitzGerald, "and, having writ/ Moves on: nor all your Piety nor Wit/Shall lure it back to cancel half a Line/Nor all your Tears wash out a Word of it." As though bent on illustrating Omar's text literally, the Parker Pen Company of New York announced, in 1958, its revolutionary new "solar pen," which would write as indelibly as the Poet had envisioned. Tiny holes in the barrel of the pen gather the sun's heat, then condense and store it. The pen uses the stored heat *to burn its writing into the paper.* How far the Parker firm has gone with this idea is something the present author has not had time to check; however, ball-points are still holding their own, including Parker's "T-Ball Jotter." Still, it's an interesting idea, with great possibilities for check-writing, holographic wills and other documents that must by their very nature defy alteration. But not for Junior's nightly homework.

9 PROBLEMS OF SOLAR ENERGY STORAGE AND CONVERSION

Because of the more or less unpredictable nature of terrestrial sunlight, even granting a certain foreknowledge based on long-range weather forecasting and climatic studies, the problem of energy storage and conversion looms as the major barrier to full-scale utilization of solar radiation.

Once this problem has been solved, however, solar energy will have arrived—in a big way. Fossil fuels and even atomic energy will have to give place to Old Sol as the number one prime mover.

According to Dr. Ghai of India (page 70), the most likely avenue of development is along the lines already charted by men like Shuman, Abbot, and others who proved the effectiveness of heating a fluid (water or heat-transfer agent) and then storing that fluid in a well-insulated reservoir or tank, improving this system by the use of heat-absorbing chemicals, vacuum or Dewar vessels, and the use of advanced types of insulating materials, such as those now being tested for space vehicles.

There is also the possibility of storing solar energy in chemical form. New types of high-energy, long-lasting chemical cells have appeared in recent years, such as mercury and magnesium cells, nickel-cadmium or cadmium-silver oxide batteries, the much publicized fuel cell, and other specialized cells now being designed for space applications. Another form of energy storage that has been tested experimentally is the breaking up of water vapor into hydrogen and oxygen by means of solar energy and the subsequent storage of the hydrogen for later use as fuel. Jesse Hobson, former director of the Stanford Research Institute, in commenting on the above method of energy storage, said "The sun does not cost us anything, and water is sufficiently abundant all over the earth. Once an economical way is found to decompose water into its gaseous constituents, an unlimited source of energy can become available. Hydrogen gas is a high quality fuel which develops intense heat when burned. Here we have a much clearer road towards opening up new sources of energy than any attempts we might make now to control the hydrogen bomb." Mr. Hobson, however, admits that it will take quite a while before economical storage of hydrogen for household consumption becomes a reality.

Experiments have indicated that flat-plate solar collectors in conjunction with solar power plants convert only about 1 percent of the received sunlight into electricity. This rate can be increased by further design improvements to about 2 percent; when parabolic mirrors or reflectors are used, the efficiency goes up to 3½ or even 5 percent. These are modest percentages, to be sure, but the amount of electricity resulting from this much solar energy is by no means small.

We have seen how solar batteries can convert sunlight directly into electric current. Similarly photovoltaic and photogalvanic cells (to be distinguished from photoelectric cells) can also be used to convert and store solar energy. Electricity is produced in photovoltaic cells when light falls upon one of the metals or oxides of a dissimilar pair. Such a photovoltaic cell consists usually of a copper disk covered on one side with a thin layer of selenium. Such a cell converts about 0.1 percent of the solar energy into electrical energy. A photogalvanic reaction develops in the boundary or barrier layer between illuminated and dark plates in a solution of thiosulfate and iron sulfate, due to the relative degree of light sensitivity of these substances, but the low rate of energy conversion raises doubts as to whether this method will ever become practical.

Considerably higher rates of energy conversion—up to 11 percent—have been achieved with the silicon photocells developed by the Bell Telephone Laboratories (page 100). In this connection, Dr. Morton B. Prince, director of the Research and Development Division of the Hoffman Semiconductor Division at Evanston, Ill., remarked that the costs of converting solar energy into electrical energy with silicon cells could be lowered within the next few years from $600 to $30 per watt.

Producing oxygen and hydrogen from water by using cerium salts as absorption agents for the transfer of thermal energy required for the dissociation of water would be an example of a practical photochemical reaction. The hydrogen and oxygen could be stored and later combined again, thus releasing stored energy but not, we hasten to add, in an uncontrolled explosion.

A thermoelement developed by Dr. Eduard Justi, professor of physics at the Braunschweig Institute of Technology, deserves to be mentioned here. It is the result of extremely painstaking research in materials and achieves a better performance than any other thermocell, photovoltaic cell or solar battery. This thermoelement consists of a small p-type rod of bismuth telluride (Bi_2Te_3) at the left and a small n-type rod of bismuth-antimony alloy at the right (90 bi, 10 Sb). At their upper ends these two small rods are connected to a blackened copper disk. In a demonstration by Dr. Justi given at the Institute in 1957, the disk was heated by an infrared radiation lamp (Philip's "Infraphil"), which, from the standpoint of entropy and photochemistry, is certainly not a high-intensity radiation source. Dr. Justi used this lamp intentionally, in preference to sunlight, to dramatize the end result. He placed the separate junctions in ice-cold water, then heated the blackened copper disk to exactly 132°F with the infrared lamp, producing exactly 100° difference in temperature between the ends of this thermocouple, which, as experts will agree, would seem hardly enough effect to start even a toy steam engine. The current produced by the thermocouple, however, was surprisingly high—55 × 300 microvolts, or 16.5 millivolts. This current, because of the minimal resistance of only a few milliohms, was sufficient to energize an electromagnet placed underneath the thermocell with about *one ampere,* so that the magnet, to the surprise of everyone in the lecture room, *picked up a one-pound weight.* It seemed uncanny that a little bit of heat from a low-frequency radiation source could accomplish this feat, converting light into mechanical energy under the eyes of the amazed onlookers.

The greater the temperature difference between the two junctions of a thermocouple, the greater is the electromotive force developed. According to Dr. Justi, temperature differences up to 450°F can be achieved by using n-materials and special solders with higher melting points. For example, an indium-tin solder (or In/Sn eutectic plus lead) has a melting point of 239°F, much lower than that of "ordinary" solder (37 Pb/63 Sn), which is 361°F. Lead itself in the pure state has a melting point of 620°F, but combining it with other elements either lowers or raises the "combined" or eutectic melting point. Silver, used as a tin substitute during World War II, when used in proportions greater than 2.5 percent, forms a eutectic with lead that melts above 700°F. Some silver solders used for brazing resist melting up to 1500°F. If the temperature difference between the thermocouple junctions is held at 450°F, for example, or 250°C, the Carnot thermal energy factor would be 250 (250 + 273) = 48 percent, which is equivalent to a 5 percent overall thermocouple efficiency or 5 percent solar-energy-conversion efficiency.

Recent Improvements in Thermocouple Efficiency. According to the April 6, 1962 issue of *Electronics* magazine,* recent efforts in the thermoelectric or thermocouple field have resulted in the development of new materials that permit conversion efficiencies as high as 12 percent and the construction of experimental units up to 5 kilowatts capacity. The author of this article, David Linden, of the U.S. Army Signal Corps Research and Development Laboratories at Fort Monmouth, N.J., states that the U.S. Navy has been testing a 250-watt, propane-fired thermoelectric generator using lead telluride for the n-leg and germanium bismuth telluride for the p-leg. The unit, which operated at a hot-junction temperature of 450°C (842°F), with a cold-junction temperature of 130°C (266°F), had an overall efficiency of 1.4 percent, although the individual thermocouples had an efficiency of 4.4 percent. Mr. Linden also states that the U.S. Army is developing a leaded-gasoline powered generator which will provide 45 watts and is expected to have a thermocouple life of 1,000 hours. The Air Force is sponsoring a program involving a solar-powered thermoelectric generator for space application, having an output of 20 watts per pound. This gives it a higher output per pound than the Army generator, which is said to weigh about 10 pounds, including fuel for 12 hours of operation.

* David Linden, "New Power Sources and Energy Converters," *Electronics,* McGraw-Hill Publishing Co., Inc., April 6, 1962, pp. 35–42.

Mr. Linden predicts that thermoelectric generators will be greatly improved in coming years, especially as to weight, size and capacity, and that existing problems of poor contact design, mechanical strength and resistance degradation will be solved through more research. Initially, he says thermoelectric generators will operate at low conversion efficiencies, but overall performance will be sufficiently high to place them in wider use inside of two or three years.

A relatively new kind of electronic device that converts heat to electrical energy directly—the thermionic converter—has opened up an entirely new field with extraordinary possibilities for solar energy. The thermionic converter, invented in 1956 by Dr. Volney C. Wilson of General Electric Company's research and development laboratories, is based on the principle of the electron or vacuum tube, which in the early days of radio was called a "thermionic valve," because it utilized the well-known Edison effect (discharge of electrons from a glowing filament in a vacuum) to control the flow of current in a circuit. The thermionic valve or vacuum tube diode (filament and plate) became our present-day amplifier tube or triode when Lee DeForest in 1907 added a third element, the grid, which controlled the flow of discharged electrons from filament to plate. It occurred to Dr. Wilson that the thermionic valve might be made to work in reverse, i.e., convert heat into current, provided the temperature of the filament could be raised high enough by mechanical means. His device consists of two metal electrodes enclosed in a vacuum, one of which is kept at a relatively low temperature while the other is raised to about 2500°F. This heat is sufficient to cause electronic discharge or "boiling" from the heated electrode, which results in a stream or current of electrons from the hot to the cold electrode. A plate connected to an external circuit intercepts this flow of current (as in the Edison effect), and by means of suitable control grids the current can be amplified and made to do work, charge storage batteries, and the like. The device thus converts heat into electricity—with efficiencies that will approach 20 percent in the next few years, and have already reached 14 percent, as described below.

Dr. Guy Suits, director of research at G.E., believes that the invention of the thermionic converter marks the beginning of an entirely new era in man's industrial and scientific development—

the direct conversion of heat into electrical energy without the use of boilers, turbines, or generators.

Increased Efficiency of Thermionic Converters. In 1960 the RCA Laboratories at Princeton, N.J., succeeded in reaching efficiencies of about 14 percent with a new three-electrode type of thermionic converter which is capable of producing electricity directly from conventional heat sources or from the heat produced by a nuclear reactor. In the earlier or vacuum type of thermionic converter, the spacing between the two electrodes—anode and cathode—was kept small, to reduce the space-charge effect. The first major improvement in this design consisted of introducing an ionized vapor, such as cesium, to neutralize the space charge and facilitate the flow of electrons. The cathode, however, had to perform the dual function of both ionizing the cesium gas and emitting electrons, and to do this effectively it had to be held at a temperature of not less than 3600°F.

RCA overcame this difficulty by adding a third electrode or element to perform the function of ionizing the cesium. Since this element does not have to give off a stream of electrons as well, it can be kept at a temperature considerably less than 3600°F, permitting the use of a cathode with higher emission characteristics. Both anode and cathode can thus be operated at temperatures of about 2000°F. RCA reported efficiencies as high as 14 percent with this improved design; as of the present writing, subsequent tests have shown efficiencies as high as 15–17 percent with cathode temperatures of only 1500°C or roughly 2700°F.

To quote *Electronics* once again on this subject, the November 17, 1961 issue of that publication stated* that thermionic converters should reach efficiencies of 20 percent within the next five years (i.e., by 1966). For space purposes, the authors claim, "these systems need highly accurate solar concentrators with concentration ratios greater than 2,000 to 1, but are potentially lighter, cheaper and smaller than solar-cell systems. The major problem is improving lifetime and reliability, although some feel that until energy storage is successfully incorporated, thermionic converters will find application in planetary probes where they could be in the sun all the time, rather than satellites. . . . A solar-thermionic system being developed by Electro-Optical Systems

* John F. Mason and Michael F. Wolff, "Missile and Space Electronics," *Electronics,* McGraw-Hill Publishing Co., Inc., November 17, 1961, pp. 106–107.

may supply 135 watts on Mariner probes; it will use a solar collector 5 feet in diameter to focus radiation onto cesium diode converters being built by Thermo-Electron Engineering Corporation."*

We have noted the solar power plant of the Austrian engineer Krenn (page 94) and its ingenious use of mercury vapor, stating that no one has since attempted to duplicate this novel arrangement. The statement is not strictly true, if we include experimental work now being done for the U.S. National Aeronautics and Space Administration (NASA), which includes a 3-kilowatt mercury-vapor turbine system ("Sunflower I") and a 15-kilowatt rubidium-vapor system, both for use in outer space. The Sunflower I power plant is being developed by Thompson Ramo Wooldridge to supply the auxiliary power requirements of the Centaur and Saturn space projects.

We will have some further words on many of the subjects covered above, as well as additional information on solar power plants and solar batteries, when we discuss space applications of solar energy (page 133).

* See below, p. 147.

10 PHOTOSYNTHESIS

Why is the grass green? As children we asked the question, but were too young to comprehend the answer. As adults we rarely give the subject a thought, taking nature's verdant mantle more or less for granted, as we do the color of our skin or hair.

But if we are pressed for an answer, certain words come to mind—"chlorophyll" and "photosynthesis." We all knew what chlorophyll was a few years back—something to put in chewing gum and mints to sweeten the breath. It even found its way into toothpaste, only to be supplanted by stannous fluoride, which looks white. We may not know how to define "photosynthesis," but at least we're sure it has nothing to do with photography. A quick check of the dictionary reveals that the word comes from the Greek *photo-,* meaning light, and *synthesis,* meaning "a putting together" or "building up." A building up of food (carbohydrates) in and by the plant through the action of light.

And "chlorophyll"? Another pair of Greek words: *chloro-,* meaning green, and *-phyll,* meaning leaf. The green coloring matter in leaves, or the plant bodies (chloroplasts) comprising it, in or by which the plant food is manufactured.

But the most important Greek root, for our purpose, is the *photo-* part.

Before going any further, it will be comforting to learn that *nobody* knows the complete answer to the question at the beginning of this chapter. Photosynthesis is still only partly understood, even by the world's best scientists.

It has been said that, of all the processes taking place on the earth—erosion, the hydrologic cycle, air-mass movements, earthquakes, volcanic action, and the like—photosynthesis is far and away the most important. The reason behind this sweeping statement is that photosynthesis *provides all living things with food,* including you and me. (Well, one might exist for a time on mushrooms and other fungi, which are *saprophytes,* without chlorophyll—but these in turn live on dead organic matter, which was produced through photosynthesis.)

The raw materials of the chemical reaction known as photosynthesis are water (H_2O) and carbon dioxide (CO_2). The plant draws the water out of the soil with its roots; the carbon dioxide is drawn in through the leaves from the surrounding air. The energy that makes these two simple compounds combine to make carbohydrates is the subject of this book—solar energy. Scientists have long known the "formula" for this reaction:

$$6CO_2 + 6H_2O \longrightarrow C_6H_{12}O_6 + 6O_2$$

carbon
dioxide   water   glucose   oxygen

The chlorophyll, which does not appear in the above equation, is a *catalyst* in the reaction; without it there is no reaction. It has been determined that the chloroplasts are the seat of the photosynthetic process, and that chlorophyll is a complex compound of hydrogen, oxygen, carbon, nitrogen and magnesium, arranged something like: $C_{55}H_{12}N_4O_5Mg$.

The rate of photosynthesis increases in direct proportion to the intensity of sunlight, starting at about 1 percent of full mid-day summer sunlight, and reaching a maximum at about 35 percent of full sunlight. It takes place on cloudy days, and even under artificial light of suitable quality. The ambient temperature is important, too, most photosynthesis in temperate zones occurring within a range of 50–90°F. Increase in temperature causes an increase in the rate of photosynthesis up to an optimum (depending on the kind of plant), which for temperate-zone species varies between 62 and 86°F. Above this maximum the rate of photosynthesis actually falls off, and too much heat can kill a plant as readily as too much cold.

Until about 1945, before the discovery and application of radio-active carbon-14 as a tracer element, the "formaldehyde" hypothesis seemed to explain the mechanism of photosynthesis better than any earlier theory. According to this, the carbon dioxide and water combine to form carbonic acid. With the aid of solar energy, the chloroplasts transform the carbonic acid into formaldehyde (HCHO) and oxygen, the latter being released and returned to the air through the leaves (transpiration). Six formaldehyde molecules were believed to combine, or polymerize, to form glucose ($C_6H_{12}O_6$), one of the simpler sugars—a "hexose," because it has 6 oxygen molecules. Actually glucose could be synthesized in the laboratory from formaldehyde, but it took a great deal of time; Adolph von Baeyer, the German chemist who first proposed the formaldehyde theory in 1870, supposed that the plant's enzymes speeded up the process in the leaves. This theory was first shaken by Samuel Ruben and Martin Kamen in 1938, when, using the isotope oxygen-18, they determined that the oxygen given off by plants came from the water molecule—not from the carbon dioxide, as assumed by the formaldehyde theory.

Ruben and Kamen, who discovered the radioisotope carbon-14 in 1945, used this versatile tracer—together with paper chromatography and autoradiography—to study the reactions further; their work was actually brought to fruition by A. A. Benson and Melvin Calvin who, using the same techniques, made some exceedingly important discoveries that unlocked age-old secrets.

First of all, they detected absolutely no formaldehyde in any photosynthetic reaction—and they studied thousands of them. But as many as 15 different substances *were* discovered in the plant cell. They determined that the first important step in the process was the formation of gyceryl phosphate from carbon dioxide and water. This is a "three-carbon" compound. Two other phosphates were found, both sugars—ribulose diphosphate and sedoheptulose phosphate ("five" and "seven" carbon compounds respectively). Enzymes were also discovered and traced with the carbon-14 isotope. The complete picture built up from Benson and Calvin's researches looks something like this:

First, carbon dioxide is added to the five-carbon ribulose diphosphate, making a six-carbon compound. The latter splits in two to form the three-carbon glyceryl phosphate. Enzyme reaction and that of the sedoheptulose phosphate helps synthesize the six-carbon glucose phosphate from the two glyceryl phosphates, and while this is going on the ribulose diphosphate is being regenerated so that it can start up again with the carbon dioxide.

The energy of the sun appears to fit into this cycle by causing the molecules of water to split into hydrogen and oxygen molecules —a process known as "photolysis," which can be performed in the laboratory with a strong current of electricity. The chlorophyll is the catalyst that makes this possible inside the plant leaves at ordinary temperatures, using only a very small portion of the incident light—and no electricity whatever.

Recent research in photosynthesis has proved that still another chemical plays an important part. It is a complicated substance called adenosine triphosphate, or ATP for short. This phosphorus compound is found in every living cell, and has been known to science since the researches of the German-born, Nobel-prize-winning American chemist Fritz Lipmann, beginning in 1941. The ATP molecule and certain similar compounds store the energy formed in carbohydrate metabolism in "packages," readily convertible into chemical energy for cell building, electrical energy for nerve impulses, or kinetic energy for muscular contraction.

In the plant, it is now believed that ATP stores the energy released by the sunlight when it splits the water molecules by photolysis, and that the energy is liberated with the help of the chlorophyll to "power" the ribulose-diphosphate-carbon-dioxide cycle.

The recent additions to our knowledge of photosynthesis have led many to believe—or at least speculate—that in the not too distant future man may be able to produce food from water and air by duplicating, on a large scale, the synthesis of food from carbon dioxide and water as just outlined. In December, 1954, the American Association for the Advancement of Science lent its support to this belief. Not long after this a group of scientists working under the leadership of Daniel L. Arnon succeeded in extracting chloroplasts and chlorophyll intact from plant cells, and used these to produce sugar from water and carbon dioxide in the laboratory—without the aid of the leaf itself or any living plant part. For the first time man had come extremely close to accomplishing something which up to that time only plants have been capable of doing.

In late 1961 Dr. Stanley Scher, associate research microbiologist at the University of California's Space Sciences Laboratory, Berkeley, California, and Lynn Sagan, graduate student in genetics, made the astounding discovery that the chloroplast *syn-*

thesizes its own genetic material and controls its own reproduction within the living plant cell. According to *Science Service,* such genetic autonomy may mean that the chloroplast once existed on its own at some time earlier in its evolution. Later, chloroplasts and certain living cells in green plants may have joined in their present mutually beneficial relationship. "With the ability to reproduce and make food, the chloroplast may actually be a cell living within a cell. If anyone can get the chloroplasts to grow and reproduce outside the 'host' cell, it will be a major first in biology. No one to date has accomplished such a feat with any subcellular unit."*

CAN MAN IMITATE THE PLANTS?

The duplication of photosynthesis on a large scale by man now seems to be a distinct possibility. With the knowledge gained in recent years, scientists can begin to concentrate on the development of a practical method—possibly by using less complicated substances than ATP, and perhaps without the aid of chloroplasts themselves.

Much remains to be done, however, before man can really manufacture food from chemicals. Yet the first big step—understanding of the basic process—has been taken. This is not to say that we know all the answers, that mother nature's closely guarded secret has now been revealed in every detail. But much has been accomplished.

Dr. Arnon has observed in this connection: "Should this conversion be possible, it would herald the beginning of a new era of unlimited surplus on our planet. Mankind would be able to tap the energy of the sunlight directly, and our dependence on green plants for food and energy would cease."

The population of the planet is now (1962) about 3 billion, and before the end of the century it will probably reach 4 billion. The problem of providing food, clothing, shelter and other necessaries for a constantly increasing population in the face of finite terrestrial resources becomes more and more Malthusian in its implications. Agricultural output can be increased, and additional food extracted from plants, animals and the sea, but in

* Science Service *Science Bulletin,* Nelson Doubleday, Inc., New York, 1962.

addition we will most certainly have to develop radically new sources of food if we are not to end by proving the eighteenth-century English economist right after all.

Contrary to popular notion, plants do not utilize sunlight on a large scale. Less than one percent of the solar energy that falls on a meadow, wheat field or vegetable garden is utilized for the production of food. The other 99 percent is either absorbed by the soil, or serves to vaporize moisture in the air, or warms the air in the vast thermodynamic process that is loosely called the weather. An engine that made use of only one percent of the supplied energy would very soon be discarded, yet if a synthetic food-producing plant were able to convert *only two percent* of the available solar energy, the total food resources of the world could be considerably increased.

Two percent is, obviously, a very modest goal. Even an efficiency of five percent would be not too much to aim at—and, if reached, then Dr. Arnon's statement about a "new era of unlimited surplus" would become a definite reality.

Dr. Howard A. Tanner, research director of the Solar Energy laboratory built by the Kettering Foundation in Yellow Springs, Ohio, in assessing the complex process of photosynthesis and the role played by solar energy, concludes that if man is to imitate the plants he must do better in the way of efficiency, regardless of how well the mechanism has served the plant kingdom for untold millenia. He notes that even a good harvest absorbs only 1 percent of the sunlight that falls on the immediate area, but contrasts this with the fact that the ability of plants to extract and absorb the minute fraction of carbon dioxide present in the atmosphere—0.03 percent—is quite phenomenal. For in order to produce one ton of carbohydrates, a ton and a half of carbon dioxide has to be absorbed, meaning all of the carbon dioxide contained in a layer of air 1,800 feet high over the agricultural area involved. Plants, especially grain plants, accomplish this manufacturing feat about once every 90 days.

The reverse of photosynthesis occurs when plants begin to use up the food they have stored in the manner outlined above. This process is called respiration, or oxidation of carbohydrates—a sequence of enzyme-controlled reactions in which the food energy is released a little at a time. The breakdown of glucose, for example, can be expressed as follows:

$$C_6H_{12}O_6 + 6O_2 \longrightarrow 6CO_2 + 6H_2O + \text{useful energy}$$

glucose   oxygen   carbon dioxide   water

The oxygen is absorbed from the atmosphere through the leaves, and the carbon dioxide is released. The energy is used by the plant in growing, but some of it is also stored in the form of plant cellular material, such as wood, which is later burned by man to produce heat energy—or else used to form the walls of his house, or ground up to make paper for books.

ROLE OF ALGAE IN PHOTOSYNTHESIS

Algae are primitive plants, members of the subkingdom Thallophyta, which contains only algae and fungi. Unlike fungi, however, algae contain chlorophyll, although they lack true roots, stems, leaves and flowers. And although the cells of all algae contain chlorophyll (which means "green leaf"), many have additional pigments which mask the chlorophyll, making the cells appear blue-green, golden brown, or red. Since there are more than 30,000 species of algae known at the present time, it is no wonder that differences of habitat, locomotion, and reproduction are found.

For example, many algae are one-celled organisms, like the blue-green variety, while others are multicellular, like Ulothrix. Some float in the water or settle to the bottom, some swim around like animals, and others grow on the trunks of trees or on rocks. Many algae form colonies of individual cells, each of which continues to live an independent life; such colonies may be flat, globular, or filamentary. Algae reproduce either by fission, asexually by spores, or sexually by gametes, involving an egg and a sperm as in animals.

The red and brown algae, better known as "seaweed," take a variety of forms, from the threadlike red algae to the gigantic forms known as kelp, which may grow to a length of 130 feet or more, and the sargasso weed, which has given its name to a large part of the Atlantic between the West Indies and the Azores. Some algae are microscopic in size, with all plant functions "subminiaturized," as in modern electronics. Protozoa and microscopic algae often get mixed up in laboratory cultures.

Algae have been the object of intensive study for over 60

years. The Carnegie Institution of Washington published not long ago a 352-page volume giving up-to-date scientific information on algal cultures alone.

To appreciate the special characteristics of algae, it helps to keep in mind that in the more highly developed plants, such as trees, the parts that serve to feed the plant make up more than half of its total dry weight. To a great extent, the structure of vascular and woody plants serves mechanical purposes—roots for holding the plant and gathering water, limbs and branches for exposing the greatest possible area of leaves, thick outer bark for protecting the cambium layer, and the trunk itself which provides structural strength and rigidity.

By contrast, the simple, mostly one-celled algae dispense with all these appurtenances, and are practically all food—food in the process of being manufactured and consumed almost simultaneously.

Furthermore, with algae the entire plant has nutritional value for both man and animals. Many small fish live entirely on algae, and the baleen whale, among the largest of mammals, exists primarily if not exclusively on algae (plankton consisting of animal as well as plant life). Dried algae, mainly the single-celled *Chlorella,* contain more than 50 percent of protein by weight—more than has been found in edible parts of any of the higher plants, including, of course, all vegetables known to man. Besides this, such protein is eminently suitable for human consumption, *because it* contains the ten amino acids that are considered of vital importance in human nutrition. Fowden has found as many as 23 amino acids in various species of algae.

A further distinguishing characteristic of algae is their low molecular weight—which accounts for their being so easily digestible. Besides being a source of oxygen, algae also return iodine to the soil, and some varieties are eaten medicinally as a preventive for goiter. The red algae *Chondrus* or "Irish moss" is made into a dessert called "sea moss farina," and kelp or "dillisk" is considered a delicacy by coastal peoples the world over. Algae are used in the preparation of soups, gelatin, chocolate milk, salad dressing and ice cream. The glutamic acid content in different types of algae amounts to 9 percent of the protein, or 4 percent of the dry weight. Glutamic acid is a protein that is used commercially in the manufacture of monosodium glutamate, the highly popular food seasoner.

Cultivation of high-protein algae in large cultures is of tremendous importance in solving the problem of food supply for our explosive population. Most countries have some sort of protein deficiency problem—either because of overabundance of carbohydrates in the popular diet, or actual scarcity of food. Obesity is one result of loading up on carbohydrates at the expense of proteins.

Algal cultures, on a truly mass-production scale, can go a long way toward correcting both dietary deficiencies and world food shortages. As the Number One entry in the algal food sweepstakes, *Chlorella pyrenoidosa,* loosely referred to as *chlorella,* seems to be especially suited for such large-scale culture in addition to possessing high nutritional value.

Algal cultures started in 1948–50 by the Stanford Research Institute in California showed that permanently growing cultures can be maintained. The firm of Arthur D. Little, Inc., of Cambridge, Mass., supported by funds from the Carnegie Corporation of New York, also started an experimental algal culture in 1952. Further research in this field has been done by Prof. Jack Mayers of the University of Texas, Dr. Robert Krause of the University of Maryland, Dr. Hiroshi Tamiya of Tokyo, and others. While many problems still remain to be solved, considerable progress is already evident.

Extensive algal cultures were started in Germany in 1950 by F. Gummert, M. E. Meffert and H. Stratmann of the Kohlenstoff-biologisches Forschungsstation (Carbon-Biological Research Laboratories) near Essen-Bredeney in the Ruhr valley, where the large amounts of carbon dioxide resulting from industrial operations have an extremely favorable effect on the growth of cultures. Pilot plants were started in the open, as well as in greenhouses. In the greenhouses, the cultures were grown in six cement tanks and two boxlike containers made of ceramic materials, while those in the open were cultivated in ditches measuring 30 feet long, 28 inches wide, 8–10 inches deep and a slight incline of about ¼ inch to the side walls. These ditches were lined with PVC (polyvinyl chloride) film, or with polyisobutylene, a plastic film with similar characteristics. When filled to a depth of about 4 to 6 inches, each ditch contained approximately 160 gallons of culture. The gas mixture for ventilation was introduced by means of iron pipes having many small holes.

The greenhouse boxes, which were from 3 to 4 feet long, 16

to 26 inches wide, and 6 to 8 inches deep, contained from 25 to 50 gallons of culture. No provision for artificial light was made, nor was it necessary to maintain constant temperatures. During the hot summer months, however, mechanical cooling equipment was provided.

The concentration of nutrients for these installations consisted of 0.034 part by weight of potassium nitrate (KNO_3), 0.0062 part by weight of potassium diphosphate (KH_2PO_4), and 0.0022 part by weight of magnesium sulfate ($MgSO_4 \cdot 7H_2O$). The pH value of these solutions was 6.1 when fresh, and increased during the growth of the cultures to between 7 and 8.

This pilot plant showed that the concentration of cells was dependent to a great extent on the intensity of incident light. Harvesting could be performed daily when light conditions were optimum. A 16-hour irradiation daily, using a 25-watt Osram lamp, proved most beneficial. The amount of gas supplied by the gas cylinders was 20 cubic feet per hour, resulting in a carbon dioxide content of only 1 per cent by volume of air.

Assuming that algae were required to supply 65 grams (2.3 ounces) of protein to every man, woman and child daily, a total algal cultural surface area of 1,500 square miles would be required to satisfy the needs of the present world population. This is an area considerably less than the size of Delaware (1,978 square miles), about a third larger than Rhode Island (1,058) and less than half the size of the island of Corsica (3,367 square miles). But more than land alone is needed; for each pound of harvested dry algae, at least two pounds of carbon dioxide and $\frac{1}{12}$ pound of nitrogen are required. And although there is sufficient carbon dioxide in the atmosphere, its concentration has to be increased many times before it can be used as an algal nutrient. How to do this inexpensively is a problem that has not yet been solved.

The State of Israel has also carried out experiments with *Chlorella* cultures, using large (1.5-gallon) Erlenmeyer flasks filled with 0.75 gallon of culture solution and placed on a balcony exposed to the air. The outer surface of the cultures, which could theoretically receive sunlight, was 70 square inches; the surface at the upper end of the cover was 27 square inches. Since light came from the side and illumination of a conical container is uneven, it was assumed that 38 square inches of the surface received direct sunlight.

Steady and constant stirring of the solution was provided by an air stream of 10 cubic feet of air per quart of culture per day. It turned out that untreated carbon dioxide had quite a poisonous effect on the algae because of the presence of sulfur dioxide, as well as traces of hydrogen sulfide. Accordingly it was found necessary to wash the gas with potassium permangate before introducing it to the culture area; on occasions when this was not done for test purposes, the experimental cultures died within one or two days.

Prof. H. von Witsch and R. Harder of the University of Göttingen achieved, in glass-wool cultures, a net yield of up to $\frac{1}{3}$ ounce (fresh weight) per quart, using the most effective strain of diatoms known at that time. By ventilating with a mixture of carbon dioxide and applying an illumination of 0.368 foot-candle (4,000 lumens per square meter), von Witsch obtained in 28 days a density of 1.6×10^{11} cells per quart of solution, corresponding to a dry mass of 3.3 grams per liter or 0.5 ounce per gallon.

The equipment necessary for starting an algal culture is simple enough. All that is needed is (1) a container with translucent surface, (2) a device for circulating the culture in the container to keep the algae from settling, (3) a thermometer and thermostat for temperature control, (4) a device for adding carbon dioxide, (5) harvesting equipment for continuous harvesting of mature algae, and (6) a means of preserving the harvested algae until they are used.

According to data published by the Botanical Department of the University of Israel, the above method has produced cell concentrations of between 80,000 and 100,000 cells per cubic millimeter, corresponding to an average harvest of between $\frac{1}{10}$ to $\frac{1}{8}$ ounce per gallon, within a time period of one to three weeks.

Algal cultures cannot sustain high temperatures. The plants do not necessarily die from too much heat, but their growth is greatly inhibited. For this reason, algal cultures should not be started in regions where the daily temperature is likely to go above 100°F.

The drying of algae is accomplished in a high-speed centrifuge. On the basis of recent experience, about 110 tons of dried algae may be harvested per acre, each year, using the methods outlined above.

In Japan, certain strains of algae have long been used for food, and some are even considered delicacies. Dr. Tamiya (page 120) reports that *Chlorella ellipsoidea* in the form of dry powder is an excellent substitute for green tea. Although very popular "straight," it is usually mixed with various teas in proportions up to 20 percent by volume. *Chlorella* mixed with buckwheat flour is also being used in Japan in the manufacture of spaghetti and similar pastes.

Beyond these food uses, *Chlorella* seems to be a bit too strong in flavor for the average human palate. Soups, especially chicken broth, disguise or palliate this taste, however; up to 15 percent of algal powder has been used in chicken broth with good results flavorwise. So-called "plankton soups" were fed to inmates of leper colonies during the years 1942–46, with spectacular results. The soups were boiled for 20 minutes, with salt added to improve the taste. The patients ranged from eight to seventy years of age, and before going on this diet their health was extremely poor. After a relatively short period of treatment their general health improved to a marked degree, with substantial gain in weight observed in previously emaciated patients.

We may bring the chapter to a close with a few comparative figures on algal production and use.

A *Chlorella* culture may produce 200 times as much protein as a soybean field of the same area.

The estimated yearly harvest of a *Chlorella* culture is 17.5 tons per acre, of which 50 percent (or 8.75 tons) is protein. Thus algae are on the average four times as rich in protein as eggs, which contain only 12.5 percent protein.

So far as large-scale production of algae is concerned, only one major problem presents itself. Labor costs for manufactured carbon dioxide are so high that the overall operation is not likely to be profitable. The use of waste gases from electric power plants might well be one means of obtaining a cheap source of carbon dioxide, but other substances in the exhaust (such as coal-tar products) would have to be removed by various methods. The Japanese have increased their area of algal culture at the shallow end of Tokyo Bay from year to year, and since the total land area needed to raise algae for the entire population of the world is relatively small, as we have seen (page 121), there is every reason to believe that large-scale, mass production of algae for human consumption will one day be completely feasible.

11 INFRARED AND ULTRAVIOLET

"Go out and soak up a little sunshine!" is the offhand advice we give our paleface friends and relatives whose work keeps them too much indoors. And when vacation time comes, we take our own advice with a vengeance—at the beach, the mountains, or even in the backyard. Some of us, to remove the stigma of an indoor complexion, have even taken to artificial suntan lotions.

Traditionally we think of people from sunny climes as being more carefree, more keenly alive than their less solarized fellow men. Sun and laughter are linked in prose and poetry, while clouds are the metaphor of melancholy:

> *King.* But now, my cousin Hamlet, and my son . . .
> How is it that the clouds still hang on you?
> *Hamlet.* Not so, my lord; I am too much in the sun.

Neapolitan love songs, the beach at Cannes, water-skiing in the Caribbean, the boardwalk at Atlantic City—these are inseparably bound up with the sun, and with pleasurable feelings, too. The sun has power to change not only man's physical condition but his emotional setup as well.

Certain physical ailments are also associated with the lack of sufficient sunlight—notably rickets and certain skin disorders, together with other so-called "deficiency diseases." Exposure to sunshine enables the body to resist these diseases by manufacturing its own vitamin D. To emend a well-worn proverb, people who live in glass houses should open the windows now and then. Ordinary window glass does not transmit health-giving ultraviolet rays. No matter how brilliantly illuminated our glass house may be, with the sun streaming through every window, unless the biologically effective rays can get through we might as well live in a burrow. So many diseases are associated with lack of sunlight that we can name only a few—anemia, scrofula, tuberculosis of the skin and bones, phlegmona or inflammation of the tissues, and furunculosis or boils. Saleeby called these the "shadow diseases." Heliotherapy is the name applied to the treatment of these diseases by exposure to fresh air and sunshine, as in solaria and sanitoria.

BIOLOGICAL EFFECTS OF SOLAR RADIATION

Light is a form of electromagnetic radiation. So also is thermal radiation, although we cannot see it. X rays, gamma rays, and cosmic rays, too, are all essentially the same kind of radiation.

What we see as white light is really a combination of violet, blue, green, yellow, orange, and red. These colors, each with its own wavelength, are known collectively as the "visible spectrum," to distinguish them from thermal, X-ray, and other forms of solar and electromagnetic radiation that are invisible. All electromagnetic radiation does not, obviously, come from the sun; your local radio station, the spark plugs of your car, and your electric range make their contributions, as well as every star in the universe.

Oddly enough, our eyes are so constructed that the part of solar radiation most beneficial to our health is completely invisible. There are many kinds of invisible radiation, but they all lie in either of two broad bands that lie above and below the range of visible radiation.

Those below the red of the solar spectrum have increasingly longer wavelengths, and range from the area immediately below the red, called the infrared region, to the feeble radiation given out by 60-cycle power lines, which have the longest wavelength of all. There is a definite relationship between wavelength and electromagnetic energy: energy is directly proportional to the *frequency* of the radiation or wave, and frequency multiplied by wavelength always equals the same constant—the constant speed of light, since all electric charges travel at the same speed in a vacuum. (To make matters a bit complicated, energy acts as though it were at the same time both a *wave* and a *particle*.) The thermal radiation given off by hot bodies, including the sun, is a form of electromagnetic radiation and obeys the same laws as those governing the propagation of radar.

Long waves are, accordingly, those propagated by low-energy sources, with low frequencies; short waves are those propagated by high-energy, high-frequency sources; these terms are, of course, relative. So-called "short-wave" radio waves are quite long in comparison to those of microwave radar, and the latter are a good deal longer than those of visible light.

Immediately below the infrared region are the longer waves of thermal radiation. The absorption of these radiations, which overlap somewhat on the electromagnetic spectrum, depends on their individual wavelengths and on the nature or material of the absorbing body. Living cellular tissue of the human body can absorb infrared rays up to a maximum of 3 microns (0.003 millimeter) long. (The upper limit of the infrared and thermal spectra is about 1,000 microns.) Glass, as we shall see later, transmits only the shorter wavelengths of the thermal and infrared regions.

A small band of rays just outside the violet are of vital importance to man. These ultraviolet rays cause reactions in our bloodstream that increase the formation of vitamin D, help build sound teeth and bones, and in general increase our resistance to disease.

Ultraviolet light, however, is not of such vital importance to plants. Contrary to earlier beliefs, it has been conclusively shown that the complex mechanism of photosynthesis does not seem to be affected to any great extent by its absence or presence. Actually a larger number of commercial greenhouses in the United States and Great Britain, as well as in some Scandinavian countries, use an "inhibited" plastic film—polyethylene or Mylar—that blocks out ultraviolet light, which otherwise would cause the plastic to decompose. Plastic greenhouses are cheaper to build and operate than glass greenhouses. And keeping out the ultraviolet makes them last longer.

Glass does transmit the heat energy of the sun, as well as the light that is so necessary to photosynthesis. But the reasons a greenhouse makes a very favorable environment for growing plants is that it discriminates between different wavelengths of thermal radiation. It lets in the heat to warm the plants, the soil, walls, pots, and tables, because this heat energy of the sun is of relatively high energy and short wavelength, ranging from about 0.8 to 1.2 microns. But when this heat is reradiated by the plants, soil, walls, pots and tables it is of a lower energy and longer wavelength, ranging from about 1.4 to 30 microns. The glass does not transmit these low-temperature, long-wave radiations nearly as well. Thus the temperature in the greenhouse builds up during the daylight hours, and the accumulated heat is stored so that the plants enjoy a more or less uniform temperature over a 24-hour period. This "greenhouse effect" takes place on a global scale, with the atmosphere acting as the "glass" of the world's greenhouse—otherwise the temperature on the dark side of the earth after nightfall would plummet to near absolute zero, as it does on the moon.

Special types of glass are made that do transmit some of the ultraviolet rays—which are also blocked by dust, smoke, fog and clouds. Sun lamps and germicidal lamps made of this special glass can give us a healthy-looking sun tan, destroy airborne and surface bacteria, spores and viruses in hospitals, restaurants, industrial plants and elsewhere.

Beyond the ultraviolet and still very much invisible are the X rays, gamma rays, and cosmic rays. We know something of the effect of the first two on plants and animals—particularly gamma rays, now that mankind has progressed so far with the atomic and hydrogen bomb. Both plants and man absorb this radiation from radioactive fallout resulting from bomb tests. Strontium 90, a long-life isotope resulting from nuclear fission, is absorbed by plants which are eaten by plants and animals; it is also absorbed directly by the bones, hence is called a "bone-seeker." It emits beta rays, while cesium 137 provides the gamma rays, which are similar to X rays only more energetic. Cosmic rays are the protons, alpha particles and heavier nuclei that bombard us from outer space; in our own atmosphere they convert a small part of our nitrogen to carbon-14. The carbon dioxide containing carbon 14 finds its way eventually into our bodies also.

The biological effect of the sun within the range from infrared to ultraviolet which we have thus briefly surveyed is indeed many-sided. The intensity and effect of the rays depend on the latitude, the time of day, the height of the atmosphere above us, and amount of dust, smog, water vapor and ionization present in our immediate vicinity. All these factors vary singly and collectively in winter and summer, in mountain and valley, in woods and meadow, in the desert and on the shore.

On tall mountains the intensity of solar radiation is nearly three times what it is in the adjoining valley. The ultraviolet rays of the sun have a bactericidal and disinfecting property, on a far grander scale than the germicidal lamps just mentioned. The ferments and toxins of bacteria can be decomposed by these ultraviolet rays; Friedberger was able to prove that *Linfa vacuna* can be sterilized without impairing their immunizing characteristics. Experiments by other scientists have confirmed these results.

A common effect of ultraviolet light on the human body is sunburn. Our skin seems to act in a manner analogous to the glass of a greenhouse, discriminating between various wavelengths of solar radiation. Ultraviolet waves have wavelengths of from approximately 0.4 to 0.015 micron, compared to the range of visible light, which is from 0.78 to 0.4 micron. (As we get to the shorter and shorter wavelengths, they are measured in *angstrom units,* one of these units being equal to 0.0001 micron, or one ten-thousandth of a micron. Thus we would write 4000 A to 150 A as the range of the ultraviolet, and 7800 to 4000 A as the range of visible light.) Ultraviolet waves of shorter wavelengths are absorbed by the protective horny layer of the epidermis, which has flattened, dead and scalelike cells. The inner layer of the epidermis, or germinative layer, has live or active cells which are injured by ultraviolet radiation of wavelength greater than 2500 A. The injured cells release chemicals, causing the capillaries to open and the skin to redden; a severe burn will cause white blood cells to accumulate and form a blister, after which the damaged skin falls off and a new epidermal layer is formed.

Solar radiation has other marked effects on the human organism. Some of these are as yet not understood. It is only recently that ergosterol, a substance present in foods and in the skin, was determined as the source of vitamin D production in the human body, a process dependent entirely on ultraviolet radiation reaching the skin. Experiments conducted by Zuntz and Durig at high altitudes proved that both muscular tissue and metabolism are stimulated by the sun, leading to the conclusion that sunlight also affects the oxidation of protein up to its transformation into oxalic and uric acid.

It is surprising that so little is known, however, about the way in which solar radiation is transmitted to the various organs of the body, including the skin, blood, bones, muscles and tissues. An early theorist named Engelmann distinguished himself by venturing the belief that the eye alone acts as a transmitter—oblivious to the fact that people blind from birth can still be pretty healthy specimens. From the evidence of X-ray photographs we know that this form of radiation penetrates through the skin down to the bones; why shouldn't the ultraviolet rays do the same thing, being adjacent to X rays on the electromagnetic spectrum? There is general agreement that the skin absorbs solar radiation over its entire surface; anyone with a good dose of sunburn doesn't need convincing on that score. We know also that prolonged, generation-to-generation exposure to sun can change the skin's pigmentation, although genetic factors are also involved. Experiments by Meirowski proved that the effect of solar radiation on the cellular nucleus produces pigment, followed by the formation of a pigmentary layer as both reserve and protection. It is well known that people with brown or dark skin are less subject to sunburn and skin infections than people with light skin, indicating some sort of defense mechanism at work in connection with the pigment.

There seems to be general agreement that the blood distributes solar energy throughout the body. Alexander and Revecz believe that the optical impulse of sunlight produces and stimulates certain reactions in the central nervous system. Experiments conducted at the Institute of Pharmacology in Vienna confirm that muscle fibers, whether contracted or uncontracted, are also influenced by solar radiation. So far as can be determined, no experiments so far have shown that solar radiation penetrates more than a fraction of a millimeter through the skin, although this seems to be enough to account for its manifold effects on the human organism. Whether or not some sort of "chain reaction" occurs to amplify or diversify these effects, or whether other organs beside the skin retain, filter or concentrate the radiation are questions that can be answered only by further research.

ARTIFICIAL SOLAR RADIATION

Countries not blessed with an abundance of sunshine are coming more and more to depend on artificial solar radiation—for medical, hygienic, and therapeutic purposes as well as for the improvement of animal livestock and, to some extent, plants.

The spectral range of solar radiation can best be attained artificially with a pure carbon-arc lamp operating at temperatures up to

7500°F. The disadvantages of these lamps are that the carbon electrodes have to be replaced from time to time, and the radiation from them is concentrated in a spot of high intensity rather than diffused over an area. Another shortcoming of carbon-arc lamps is that they produce little or no ultraviolet radiation. They are, however, highly actinic and find wide use in blueprint shops and photoengraving work.

Lamps that do generate ultraviolet as well as visible light are a welcome and valuable substitute for the genuine article, especially in crowded metropolitan centers where the ultraviolet is often filtered out by haze and dust. Low-pressure mercury lamps are being used with good results for sterilizing the air in classrooms, hospital sickrooms and operating rooms, theaters and auditoriums, indoor swimming pools, and the like. They are made of quartz glass as "Vita" glass, and yield fairly large amounts of ultraviolet radiation.

A high-pressure mercury lamp made by the Quartz Lamp Company of Hanau consists of a vacuum tube of quartz glass with an electrode at each end, equipped with a self-starting device. The current is introduced into the tube by means of a molybdenum foil a few millimeters wide, which is fused hermetically into the tube during manufacture. The tube contains traces of an inert gas and a small pool of mercury. When ignited, an incandescent arc first forms which warms the mercury and slowly vaporizes it. The vapor, which is then ionized, becomes a current-carrying conductor and fills the entire tube with a brilliant glow. A large part of the energy emitted by such lamps is in the form of ultraviolet light. General Electric, Westinghouse, Sylvania and other large American firms produce similar types of mercury-vapor lamps. Some of these lamps, if used as a professional therapeutic generator, can give off such strong ultraviolet radiation that an exposure of a minute or less can produce a good sunburn.

The ordinary sun lamps one buys in the drugstore for home use are much less powerful, requiring about ten to fifteen minutes to produce a light sunburn. They screw into a standard light socket and look like ordinary incandescent floodlight bulbs, but inside the special glass envelope they contain a small mercury arc in a tiny quartz tube, surrounded by a tungsten filament. The light from these lamps resembles that of ordinary incandescent lamps, because one can't see the "enriching" ultraviolet radiation provided by the tiny mercury arc.

About the effect of solar or artificial solar radiation on the basal metabolism of the human body there is some difference of opinion. Lotz claims to have found that ultraviolet radiation (whether natural or artificial) results in an immediate lowering of the metabolic rate, and that such lowering can be precipitated when the ratio of ultraviolet to infrared rays is on the order of 1:114. In addition, Lippross has found that radiation with visible long-wave rays and infrared rays immediately raises the skin temperature, not merely locally but over the whole organism even when the radiation itself is local. This increase in temperature, he claims, extends also to the musculature, and penetrations by infrared rays to a depth of 1½ inches were measured by him. Immediate improvement in blood circulation and vascular action is said to have followed, accompanied by a general increase of the entire metabolism. Furthermore, ultraviolet radiation was said to have improved blood count in anemia.

Breeders of young animals are using ultraviolet radiation, both natural and artificial, in combating rickets and bone deficiencies —with good results. The use of infrared radiation in chicken farming is becoming a standard feature in many areas. Practical experience has been gained on the basis of using three infrared lamps in raising from 200 to 300 chickens, following a program of gradually increasing the height of the lamps above the floor of the brooder from 28 to 48 inches in steps of 4 inches, over a period of 6 to 8 weeks. At the end of this period one of the lamps was turned off; after 10 weeks, the second, and after 14 weeks the third, giving a total of 14 weeks of gradually diminishing infrared radiation. The same kind of therapeutic radiation can be used in raising lambs, pigs, and other small animals.

INFRARED RADIATION IN INDUSTRY

The industrial uses of infrared radiation are numerous and varied, from the roasting of coffee and the curing of tobacco to the lacquering of automobiles and the enameling of refrigerators. Not only is the time for drying greatly reduced with infrared lamps, but their number and placement makes for more uniform drying or baking on mass-production lines and other large-scale operations. For example, in coremaking or sand casting, cores can be dried by infrared radiation in 25 minutes or less, compared with one hour for air drying. Similarly, epoxy and other resin molds can be "cured" in less time, with reduced hazards as compared with oven or flame heating.

More spectacular is the fact that the drying of corrugated plastic roofing made from glass fiber or acrylic resins dries or "cures" in a mere six minutes with infrared heat; air drying would take an estimated forty-eight hours! In the printing industry, infrared radiation is used to fast-dry printing inks in place of gas flames or drying agents that might impair their consistency; it even makes the practice of "slip-sheeting" unnecessary in most cases.

Absorbent materials dry much faster with infrared radiation than by warm air. The infrared heat penetrates the substance and causes it to dry from the inside out, rather than drying deceptively on the surface while remaining moist underneath.

In some large European cities infrared heating has been installed under store awnings to provide heat for windowshoppers. This kind of heat, conveyed by special tubular conductors, is not to be confused with the so-called "radiant heating" of sidewalks and floors by concealed steam or electric lines. In Paris two types of infrared tubes are in use for the purpose—one 32 inches long with a capacity of 2 kilowatts, the other 54 inches with a 4-kw capacity. Twenty-five of the smaller and twenty-six of the larger were installed above ground at 5- and 8-foot intervals respectively, using over 400 feet of cable and requiring an additional installed capacity of some 300 kw.

Hundreds of other examples of infrared heating in industry and elsewhere might be cited, but even including these it must be admitted that infrared utilization has hardly begun. One major reason for the lack of spectacular progress in this area is that the effects of this type of heating are as yet not fully known or appreciated—especially radiation in the range of from 1 to 10 microns. Likewise, the field of ultraviolet radiation and its possible applications deserves to be further explored.

12 SOLAR ENERGY AND SPACE EXPLORATION

With some 40 artificial satellites in orbit around the earth at the present time (1962), we tend to forget the role played by rocketry in the exploration of space. Had it not been for this work going back to the late 1930s, neither Major Ghermann Titov nor Colonel John Glenn would have been able to orbit the earth in their respective space capsules. It is very unlikely, too, that world scientists would know so much about the sun as they do at the present time.

PIONEERING DISCOVERIES OF ROCKETRY

The "Star Spangled Banner," written in 1814, refers to "the rocket's red glare," some 500 years after the Chinese had developed rockets to a practical level as a military weapon. By 1929, Robert H. Goddard in America had demonstrated the feasibility of sending instrumented rocket missiles into the upper atmosphere. About the same time men like Hermann Oberth, Walter Hohmann and Franz von Hoefft in Germany, Robert Esnault-Pelterie and André Hirsch of France, and Count Guido von Pirquet of Austria were making remarkable contributions to the field. Russia had established a genuine "first" with the brilliant theoretical work of Konstantin Ziolkovsky, who as early as 1903 had made the first plans and calculations for a liquid-propellant rocket engine, continuing his design work until his death in 1935.

In 1933 the German Army established the world's first guided missile research center at Peenemünde, first under the direction of Walter Dornberger, later under Wernher von Braun—the results of which are too well known to bear repeating here, though no less world-shaking in their ultimate significance. Here was born and fired the A-4 military rocket which later came to be known to the world as the V-2—46 feet long, 5 feet in diameter, weighing 14 tons and developing 56,000 pounds of thrust to carry it 200 miles in five minutes.

The United States and Great Britain, among others, had developed a variety of aircraft and other small rockets, including the famed "bazooka" of 1943 and "calliope" multiple rocket launchers, known also in Russia as the "Stalin Organ." At the end of the war, the United States removed about 100 V-2 rockets from Peenemünde, and the production facilities were then turned over to the occupying Soviet troops. By December 17, 1946, a team of U.S. rocket experts had successfully launched its first captured V-2 to a height of 114 miles. In February of 1949 another V-2, acting as a first stage for a *WAC-Corporal* rocket, raised the latter to a new world altitude record of 242 miles.

At present, seven nations are using rockets for exploration and research purposes—the United States, the Soviet Union, Great Britain, France, Japan, Canada and Australia. Some 200 or more exploratory rockets were fired by the U.S. alone during the International Geophysical Year (1957–1958), from bases in the Arctic, Antarctic, Pacific and elsewhere. In this program the following rockets were used by the United States:

(1) The *Aerobee,* designed for carrying an instrument load of 150 to 200 pounds to a height of about 60 miles.

(2) The *Aerobee-Hi,* carrying the same useful load but to a height of 200 miles.

(3) The *Nike-Cajun,* a solid-fuel multistage rocket carrying a useful load of 40 pounds to a height of 100 miles.

(4) The *Nike-Deacon,* with a second stage called the *Dan,* carrying a useful load of 40 pounds to a height of 80 miles.

(5) Balloon-launched *Deacon* missiles using the *Skylark* polyethylene balloon that carried the *Deacon* to a height of 50,000 feet before launching, together with similar combinations called *Rockoons,* the combinations giving a maximum altitude of about 70–80 miles, although in *Project Farside* the height reached by balloon-launched rockets was as great as 2,750 miles.

During the IGY, which was extended through 1959 to continue data-collecting activities in certain areas, scientists of more than 60 nations cooperated in a massive effort to solve some of the mysteries of the earth and space. In December of 1958 Prof. Marcel Nicolet, Secretary-General of IGY, said: "At the beginning of this year we had only a partial knowledge of the composition of the upper atmosphere up to a height of 124 miles. But thanks to the Russian and American rockets and satellites, we now have a detailed knowledge of the atmosphere to a height of close to 500 miles." He was referring, of course, to the extraordinary series of Russian and American rocket and satellite launchings from October of 1957 to December of 1958: *Sputnik I,* launched October 4, 1957; *Sputnik II,* launched November 3, 1957; the U.S. *Project Farside,* a series of six launchings of four-stage rockets from balloons, with the highest shot estimated at 3,000 miles made during September and October of 1957; *Explorer I,* the first successful U.S. satellite, put into orbit on January 31, 1958 from Cape Canaveral; *Vanguard I,* the second American satellite, put in orbit on March 17, 1958; *Explorer III,* the third successful U.S. satellite, fired and orbited on March 26, 1958 (after No. *II* had failed to orbit); *Explorer IV,* fourth American satellite, orbited on July 26. Meanwhile Russia's *Sputnik III* had gone into orbit on May 15, after which there was a lull until August 27, when Russia fired a 3,726-lb rocket from the Kizil Kum desert to a height of 280 miles, carrying two dogs, both of which were recovered alive. Then on October 11 the U.S. took the stage again with the Pioneer I lunar probe, which was launched at Cape Canaveral and reached an altitude of 71,300 miles; followed this up on December 6 with another, the Pioneer III, which reached 66,654 miles and discovered the Van Allen belt in passing; then, just in time for President Eisenhower's taped Christmas greeting, launched the 8,800-pound Atlas intercontinental ballistic missile (ICBM), putting the entire rocket in orbit, tape recorder and all, on December 18, 1958. Surely the year 1958 was one of the great landmarks in man's exploration of space!

Of all the satellites mentioned in the above paragraph, only *Explorer I* and *Vanguard I* are still circling the earth. (Of *Vanguard I* we have more to say on page 145 below.)

Professor Nicolet warned that it would take years to analyze the data acquired by these rocket and satellite shots and by the land, sea and air explorations of the other 60 nations during the

IGY. "It will keep researchers busy until the year 2058," he said.

In a similar vein, Dr. Richard Porter, former director of the technical committee for the Earth Satellite Program, said that the attempted exploration of radiation reaching the earth from outer space, especially solar radiation, by shooting rockets from the ground up through the atmosphere, was like attempting to reconstruct the history of long-dead cultures on the basis of a few fragments of tools and potsherds found with rubble and other remnants in excavations, aided only by a superficial knowledge and secondary proofs. Many years of analysis and painstaking piecing together of facts and fragments are required before the data becomes intelligible and significant.

To bring the record up to date so far as possible, here is a quick summary of the major exploratory rocket shots, lunar probes and satellites placed in orbit from January, 1959 to June, 1962:

Country	Date	Name of Rocket or Satellite and Results of Flight
SOVIET UNION	1/2/59	*Lunik I* lunar probe; missed moon and went into orbit around sun; weight, 3,245 lb.
UNITED STATES	2/17/59	*Vanguard II*. For studying cloud cover; apogee 2,052 miles. Still in orbit.
UNITED STATES	3/3/59	*Pioneer IV*. Lunar probe, missed moon and went into orbit around sun.
SOVIET UNION	7/2/59	Single-stage liquid fuel rocket carried 4,400-lb payload 200 miles, including two dogs and hare, all recovered alive.
UNITED STATES	7/7/59	Five-stage *Javelin* rocket, 45 lb. of instruments carried to 600 miles; also *Strongarm* rocket, 25 lb to 470 miles.
SOVIET UNION	9/12/59	*Lunik II*. Lunar probe, 860 lb., impacted on moon, studied magnetic fields of earth and moon, space particles, cosmic rays.
UNITED STATES	9/18/59	*Vanguard III*, surveyed earth's magnetic field, located edge of Van Allen belt; still orbiting.
SOVIET UNION	10/4/59	*Lunik III*. Circled moon and earth, photographed moon's far side.

UNITED STATES	10/13/59	*Explorer VII*. Collected data on radiation and magnetic storms; detected weather patterns. Confirmed fact that radiation intensity decreases enormously in the exterior Van Allen belt when entering the ionized gas cloud. The solar gas cloud penetrating into the exterior Van Allen belt causes ionized particles captured there to be injected into the upper atmosphere of the earth, with greatest density near the poles—producing the so-called polar lights. This was the first time that the relation between the solar gas cloud and polar lights was demonstrated.
UNITED STATES	11/7/59	*Discoverer VII*. Studied communication, cosmic radiation.
UNITED STATES	11/10/59	Five-stage *Strongarm* rocket carried instrument payload to 1,050 miles.
UNITED STATES	3/11/60	*Pioneer V* space probe. Solar orbit; data on solar flares, cosmic radiation, and magnetic fields. Transmitted data from 22.5 million miles.
UNITED STATES	4/1/60	*Tiros I* weather satellite. Took thousands of cloud-cover pictures and relayed back to earth. Still orbiting and transmitting pictures.
UNITED STATES	4/13/60	*Transit IB* global navigation satellite. Still orbiting.
UNITED STATES	5/24/60	*Midas II* infrared scanner and detection satellite. 5000 lb. Scanning telemetry failed after two days. Still orbiting.
UNITED STATES	8/12/60	*Echo I* passive communications satellite including voice and telephone transmission. Still orbiting.
SOVIET UNION	8/19/60	*Sputnik V*. Tested vehicle for manned space flight and recovered capsule after 18th orbit.
UNITED STATES	11/3/60	*Explorer VIII*. Ionosphere measurements and study of micrometeorites. Ascertained that the ionosphere is at

least 1,600 to 2,000 miles higher than previously supposed. Discovered that lower regions of ionosphere are much disturbed by solar eruptions and magnetic storms.

UNITED STATES 11/23/60   *Tiros II*. Same purpose as *Tiros I*. Not transmitting but still orbiting.

UNITED STATES 12/20/60   *Discoverer XIX*. Studied atmospheric phenomena, and infrared radiation.

UNITED STATES 1/31/61   *Samos II*. Atmospheric and earth studies; first R&D reconnaissance satellite. Still orbiting. Weight, 4,100 lb.

SOVIET UNION 2/4/61   *Sputnik VII*. Tested 7-ton satellite in orbit.

SOVIET UNION 2/12/61   *Sputnik VIII*. Venus probe, passed planet and went into orbit around sun. Weight, 1,419 lb. Still in orbit.

UNITED STATES 2/18/61   *Discoverer XXI*. Infrared radiation studies of earth. Restarted Agena engine in space for first time. Still in orbit.

SOVIET UNION 4/12/61   *Vostok I*. Yuri Gagarin's historic flight; first manned orbit of earth; recovered after one orbit.

UNITED STATES 4/27/61   *Explorer XI*. Orbited a special telescope for mapping gamma radiation from stars as absorbed in earth's atmosphere. Surprised scientists by recording that gamma-ray activity in free space is only 1/1,000 of theoretical assumption.

UNITED STATES 5/5/61   *Freedom VII Mercury Capsule*. First U.S. astronaut in space, Lt. Cmdr. Alan B. Shepard reached 116.5 miles, 320 mile range, recovered with capsule. *Liberty Bell VII*, with Captain Virgil I. Grissom, 118 miles high on 7/21/61; capsule lost.

UNITED STATES 7/12/61   *Tiros III*. TV pictures of clouds and other meteorological data. Still transmitting.

SOVIET UNION 8/6/61	*Vostok II*. Second manned orbital flight; Maj. Ghermann Titov successfully made 18 orbits of earth.
UNITED STATES 8/15/61	*Explorer XII*. Studies of solar wind, Van Allen belt. Equipped with magnetometer, electron spectrometer and analyzer for slow protons. Measurements confirmed that "magnetosphere" (new name for Van Allen belt) captures particles of various energy levels and different densities which are emitted from sun as ionized plasma. "Capturing zone" reported at distance of 32,000 miles from earth; evidently much influenced by plasma clouds emitted from sun. Above this zone, a turbulent area of "solar storms" noted.
UNITED STATES 10/21/61	*Midas IV*. Infrared scanning early-warning satellite; 3,500 lb. Still transmitting.
UNITED STATES 2/20/62	*Friendship VII Mercury Capsule*. First U.S. manned orbital flight. Lt. Col. John H. Glenn made three successful orbits of earth with recovery of capsule and all instruments.
UNITED STATES 3/7/62	*OSO I*. Orbiting Solar Observatory of National Aeronautics and Space Administration. Weight, 458 lb. Studies of earth-sun relationship, solar storms, solar spectrum, etc. Azimuth accuracy in orbit, 0.6 minute. On May 22, after 1,138 orbits, malfunction of spin control system caused satellite to spin up to a point where servo system could no longer orient instruments and solar cells toward sun; batteries in continually discharged state and satellite no longer sending useful data.
UNITED STATES 5/24/62	*Aurora VII Mercury Capsule*. Second U.S. manned orbital flight. Lt. Cmdr.

Scott Carpenter made three successful orbits of earth with recovery of capsule and all instruments; overshot landing area by 200 miles.

UNITED STATES 5/26/62　*Ranger IV.* This 730-lb vehicle designed to send pictures of the moon's surface to earth was launched on April 23, but the solar panels which were to have powered its telemetry system failed to lock on the sun; tracking stations established that it had landed on the far side of the moon on April 26, just south of the lunar equator.

UNITED STATES 7/10/62　*Telstar I.* First privately owned communications satellite built by American Telephone & Telegraph Company and launched at their expense by National Aeronautical and Space Administration; transmitted live TV across Atlantic in both directions on July 23. Powered by solar batteries.

UNITED STATES 7/25/63　*Caleb* rocket. Two-stage solid-fuel rocket with 150 lb of radiation instruments to study composition of upper atmosphere and solar radiation. Altitude reached, 1,000 miles; launched from F4H Phantom fighter aircraft at 35,841 ft over Point Mugu, Calif.

SOVIET UNION 7/28/63　*Cosmos VII.* Seventh in series of Soviet scientific satellites, first of which was launched March 16, 1962; no information released on any of these satellites.

SOVIET UNION 8/11/62　*Vostok III.* Manned orbital flight of Andrian Grigorevich Nikolayev, followed on August 12 by *Vostok IV* carrying Pavel Romanovich Popovich in same orbit. No rendezvous was reported, although one may have been attempted. *Vostok III* performed 64 orbits, Vostok IV, 48.

UNITED STATES 8/27/62   *Mariner II.* Venus space probe, 447-lb instrument satellite launched by Atlas-Agena rocket; trajectory and course altered by signals September 4 from Goldstone, Calif. Deep Space Facility; passed within 22,000 miles of Venus on December 14; gave surface temperature readings of over 800°F on both "light" and "dark" sides.

DOMINION OF CANADA
9/27/62   *Alouette.* Canadian-built scientific satellite, launched in polar orbit by U.S. (NASA), first satellite completely designed and built by any nation other than U.S. and Soviet Union; 320-lb spheroid, designed to investigate ionosphere and study radio "noise."

UNITED STATES 10/2/62   *Explorer XIV.* Radiation research satellite, apogee of 61,000 miles and perigee of only 175 miles; orbital period, 36 hours; estimated lifetime, 75 years.

UNITED STATES 10/3/62   *Sigma 7.* Manned orbital flight of Cmdr. Walter M. Schirra in Mercury capsule; completed six orbits of the earth and landed in Pacific Ocean four miles from Carrier *Kearsarge.*

SOVIET UNION 10/17/62   *Cosmos X.* Tenth in the Soviet Union's secret *Cosmos* series, this one was reported to perform "radiation research." Followed on October 21 by *Cosmos XI.*

UNITED STATES 5/15/63   *Faith 7.* Manned orbital flight of Maj. Gordon Cooper in Mercury capsule; completed 22 orbits of the earth and landed in Pacific Ocean on May 16 —two miles from Carrier *Kearsarge.*

SOVIET UNION 6/14/63   *Vostok V.* Manned orbital flight of Valery Bykovsky, followed 45 hours later by *Vostok VI,* carrying first woman astronaut Valentina Tereshkova. No rendezvous reported although one was evidently planned, yet the two orbits were considerably different. Bykovsky landed after 82 orbits, Miss Tereshkova after 44—both on June 19.

The advantage of exploratory rockets and artificial satellites consists in the fact that scientific instruments can be brought in direct contact with the upper layers of the atmosphere, and beyond it, so that we may observe either the atmosphere itself or the planets and stars beyond it without its interference. Thus we can study, for example, the effects of partial currents and radiation on the ionosphere, or make special studies of solar flares and the corona, as was done with the American *OSO I* or Orbiting Astronomical Laboratory. Manned orbital flights collect considerable data on solar radiation and related phenomena.

Even prior to the International Geophysical Year, the United States had launched 29 exploratory rockets from the base at Fort Churchill, Ontario, jointly operated by the U.S. and Canada, as well as from White Sands, New Mexico and the island of Guam, and from ships off the coast of California and in the North Atlantic.

In May, 1949 the Soviet Union launched "the first rocket to be sent vertically into space," which reached a height of 70 miles. The instrument load in several rockets of this type was between 260 and 280 pounds. Later the Russians were able to increase this instrument payload to as much as 3,300 pounds, far beyond the launch capacities of the U.S. at that time. In several cases of geophysical rocket launchings, provisions were made to have the instruments and/or animals returned to earth by parachute. In May, 1957 a heavily instrumented Soviet rocket weighing 4,800 pounds reached a height of 130 miles, with instruments and animals returning safely. On February 21, 1958, a one-stage geophysical rocket with instruments weighing 3,400 pounds was fired by Soviet rocketeers to a height of 293 miles.

Soviet scientists were able to determine the composition of ions in rarefied gases as a result of these flights, using a radio-frequency mass-spectrograph. The positive-ion concentration was measured by an ion trap mounted on the surface of the rockets. The method of sounding was used for measuring electron temperature, and a dispersion interferometer determined the ion concentration in the different parts of the ionosphere. The solar spectrum in the ultraviolet range was photographed with a spectroheliometer.

The data provided by these measuring devices were either transmitted to ground stations by radiotelemetry or recorded on tape and recovered on landing. In measuring the ionic composition and concentration of the atmosphere at altitudes of from 65 to 130 miles, Soviet scientists found that ions with a mass number of 30—presumably ions of nitric oxide—predominate at such heights, while at the upper reaches of the flight range ions with a mass number of 16—presumably oxygen ions—were registered. A concentration of one million electrons per cubic centimeter was found to exist at an altitude of 290 miles.

The method applied in Soviet experiments is characterized by the use of shorter radio waves which considerably minimize the effect of the earth's magnetic field on the recorded data.

U.S. scientists were the first to measure, using *Dan* rockets, the ultraviolet and X-ray radiation emitted by the sun during the violent solar flares of July and August, 1957. According to published reports, these data will help clarify the problem of the precise connection between solar eruptions and radio interference. The *OSO I* and other solar-observation satellites now in orbit will greatly contribute to our knowledge of the sun in these and other areas.

With the aid of rockets launched from San Nicholas Island off the coast of California toward the end of 1957, it has been determined that after a violent solar eruption the temperature of the solar atmosphere above a flare increases about fifteenfold. It is assumed that due to this enormous heat rise the solar gases suddenly begin to radiate X rays, which reach the earth with the velocity of light and wreak havoc with radio and telephonic communications. The temperatures involved in these solar flares exceed *one million degrees centigrade.*

During experiments with high-altitude rockets launched from both the Arctic and Antarctic, certain energy particles have been discovered which are regarded as the trigger impulses for the aurora displays. British scientists have found that polar lights always appear simultaneously both in the Northern and Southern hemispheres, thus proving previously advanced theories.

By using *Aerobee* rockets, American scientists found that high above the earth's surface winter winds reach velocities of up to 300 miles an hour. Experiments with rockets conducted near

Greenland in August, 1957, proved that massive layers of electricity exist at an altitude of about 55 miles above both poles, especially during magnetic storms. These "layers" were found to be about three miles thick. A more recent discovery, based on rocketry data gleaned between 1958 and 1960, points to the existence of two vast belts of high-energy radiation around the equatorial regions of the earth, known as the Van Allen radiation belt (or "magnetosphere"), after the scientist who predicted their existence. They extend in two clearly defined zones or belts, one at 8,000 miles distant and the second, and larger one, at from 12,000 to 16,000 miles. Whether or not this radiation is so harmful as to preclude space flight through it has been much debated but not yet settled at this writing. (More recent data on the Van Allen belt is given under *Explorer* VII, VIII, XII and XIV in the summary list, pp. 137–141.)

A report by Hugh Odishaw, director of the American IGY Committee, states that rockets sent up into the ionosphere in July, 1957 provided data that confirmed the formation of an additional ionized layer 12 miles below the normally conductive layer, the so-called D layer, presumably due to the short X rays emitted by solar flares.

According to measurements carried out at the Mount Wilson observatory, the magnetic fields on the solar surface are probably 8,000 times stronger than those at the earth's equator. This finding is of great importance to the theory that these magnetic fields play a large part in the genesis and growth of solar storms and prominences. The currents of energy "injected" into the upper layers of our atmosphere are obviously capable of creating violent weather disturbances near the earth's surface. Intensive research is still being carried on to explain the functioning of the transmitting mechanism for these energy currents from the outer layers of the exosphere to the lower layers of the troposphere, where the weather really makes itself manifest to us.

SOLAR POWER IN SPACE RESEARCH

Space rockets and satellites not only enrich our knowledge about the sun and its relation to the earth—but also provide additional opportunities for the utilization of solar energy for their own components and power sources. There is something so

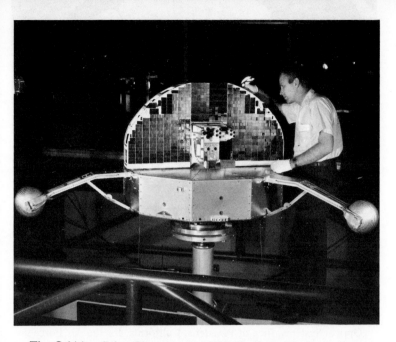

The Orbiting Solar Observatory (OSO-I) of the National Aeronautics and Space Administration. Weighing 458 pounds, with 30,000 solar cells mounted on two modularized paddles maintained normal to the sunlight, this satellite was launched on March 7, 1962 to obtain information on the sun's composition, earth-sun relationships, electromagnetic radiation, and related celestial phenomena. After about ten weeks in orbit, OSO-I lost ability to orient solar cells toward sun; the batteries were in a continually discharged state, but the satellite's major telemetry and command systems were still "Go" a year later. A great deal of useful knowledge, however, was accumulated in the 1,138 orbits before the malfunction occurred, and is still being analyzed. Designed, developed, and constructed by Ball Brothers Research Corporation of Industrial Park, Boulder, Colorado, for NASA's Goddard Space Flight Center. (*Ball Brothers Research Corp.*)

Opposite, photovoltaic spacecraft power system developed by Electro-Optical Systems, Inc., of Pasadena, California. Lightweight mirrors are used to increase the solar flux per unit panel area by 170 percent as compared with normal solar panel output. The 50 watts delivered by the mirror-panel combination is more than 2.3 times the power output of the panel itself. Built for the Flight Accessories Laboratory of the U.S. Air Force's Aeronautical Systems Division, the system is designed to provide lower weight and less cost in solar-powered space exploration. The optically accurate flat mirrors are designed to fold down on the solar panel during launch, and consist of electroformed metal foil supported by tubular metal frames. (*Electro-Optical Systems, Inc.*)

Lightweight, unfurlable solar collector developed by Electro-Optical Systems, Inc., of Pasadena, California, for the Air Force's Aeronautical Systems Division. This device can be completely closed (inset) and then opened like a flower in space to concentrate heat for thermoelectric or solar dynamic power-conversion systems. Feasibility model shown here weighs approximately 2.5 lb excluding actuator and support. The device folds up to fit inside the nose cone of a space vehicle and unfolds in space to collect solar energy. (*Electro-Optical Systems, Inc.*)

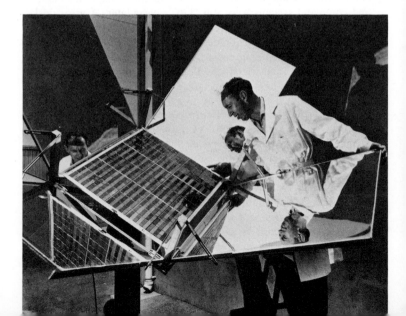

eminently logical in the fact that a device sent up to study the sun should be powered by the sun—indeed, to drive itself with solar power, as some space vehicles will be shortly capable of doing.

One of the best examples of what we mean is the highly successful use of solar batteries on the historic *Vanguard I* (page 135), launched over four years ago as of this writing *and still transmitting*. Many other satellites since that much-awaited launching on March 17, 1958 have successfully used solar cells, including *Pioneer V, Explorer VI, Transit VII, Tiros I, II,* and *III,* and *Courier.* Designs of solar batteries with capacities up to 600 watts are under consideration for *Advent* and other large communication satellites.

The estimated life of *Vanguard I* is from 200 to a thousand years. Its nearest approach to the earth, or perigee, is 404 miles, and its apogee is 2,452 miles. It takes 133.9 minutes to orbit the earth. Its solar batteries provide current for the short-wave, vhf (very high frequency) transmitter operating on a wavelength of 108.03 megacycles.

Each of the six rectangular solar batteries, which project ¾ inch from the 3¼-pound, 6½-inch sphere takes up about 3½ square inches of its outer surface. Each battery consists of 18 silicon cells, and each cell is 2 cm long by 0.5 cm wide and 0.06 cm thick. In turn, these tiny disks are composed of two silicon layers of different conductivities. The six solar batteries have a total capacity of 5 milliwatts, sufficient to power *Vanguard*'s signal for reception at apogee.

The solar batteries, which are covered with special heat-resisting glass as protection against cosmic particles, solar heat and micrometeorite dust, were distributed evenly over the surface of the hollow sphere so as to absorb as much solar energy as possible at any given attitude. About a tenth of the incident energy is converted into electric current, the remainder being lost to heating and reradiation. The cells can operate at temperatures up to 180°F, but higher temperatures reduce their efficiency. Were it not for the protective glass cover, erosion by micrometeorite dust would lower their output by as much as 30 percent.

The Vanguard's solar cells were developed by the U.S. Army Signal Corps Research and Development Laboratory at Fort Monmouth, N.J., under the direction of Dr. Hans Ziegler. According to David Linden, R&D engineer at this laboratory, the theoretical efficiency of the solar cell is about 22 percent, although the efficiency of cells now in production has leveled off to 10–12 percent, with some going as high as 14 percent. At full sunlight on the earth's surface, the output of present-day solar cells is about 10 milliwatts per square centimeter, or about 40 watts per pound. (By way of comparison, the solar energy reaching the earth in full sunlight is about 1,000 watts per square meter.) Present-day solar cells for rockets and satellites have an operating voltage of about 0.4 volt and are connected in series-parallel to provide the required total current. The use of solar cells on the ground is less efficient, partly because the relative cost of them is higher. However, one manufacturer is marketing a transistorized radio that works on solar cells, and increased mass production is bound to bring the price down.

Explorer VI, launched August 7, 1959, used 8,000 solar cells for transmitting back TV pictures of cloud cover. *OSO I,* NASA's Orbiting Solar Observatory, launched March 7, 1962, has 30,000 cells mounted on two modularized paddles maintained normal to the sunlight at all times. Groups of cells are switched in and out of the circuit either automatically or by ground control, depending on system requirements. (On May 22, 1962, OSO-I lost its ability to orient the solar-cell paddles to the sun, but continued in orbit with many of its systems still functioning.)

Gallium arsenide cells have been developed experimentally and show a theoretical efficiency of 25 percent. Cadmium sulfide has also been used to provide a lighter-weight solar cell at lower cost, although with considerably lower efficiency. A great deal of research work is at present under way in the United States to improve the output and efficiency of solar cells.

Solar Energy Converters for Space Use. Electro-Optical Systems, Inc., of Pasadena, Calif., has designed and built a number of working models of solar collectors for use in thermoelectric or solar dynamic power systems in space, particularly on interplanetary probes. One of these, delivered in August, 1961 to the U.S. Air Force's Aeronautical Accessories Laboratory of the Aeronautical Systems Division, is a lightweight, petal-type expandable or "unfurlable" collector of parabolic configuration which is 52 inches in diameter when expanded. It consists of 18 reflecting petals circularly arranged and hinged to an actuating assembly at the center of the array. The collector, which weighs about 2½ pounds without assembly or support, can be expanded from a furled position in approximately 20 seconds, according to Charles W. Stephens, Electro-Optical design engineer.

The petal collector can achieve a concentration ratio of at least 2,000. Solar rays are focused on an absorber at the focus, which has an area of about 1 inch. Collector petals, made of nickel and overcoated with aluminum, have a total reflecting surface of about 13 square feet. Efficiency of the collector has been estimated to lie between 60 and 80 percent, depending on the conversion system used and the system operating temperature. It is expected that micrometeorite dust would degrade the reflectivity of the mirror by about one percent a year in a 300-mile earth orbit.

Another type of solar energy converter designed by Electro-Optical for Mariner-class interplanetary probes consists of a 5-foot collector weighing 25 pounds, which focuses solar energy into a cavity to heat several cesium-vapor thermionic converters. The system is designed to generate 135 watts in the vicinity of Mars. Other solar energy converters for space use are being designed for the Air Force by the National Research Corporation under the direction of Professor T. Gold of Cornell University.

United Nations Conference of 1961. More than 500 delegates from seventy-one UN countries and territories attended a ten-day United Nations Conference on New Sources of Energy beginning on August 23, 1961 at Rome, Italy. The objective of the conference was to help determine how underdeveloped countries may best utilize unconventional sources of energy in their industrial development.

Mr. Roger E. Gaumer, of Lockheed Missiles and Space Division, Lockheed Aircraft Corporation, Sunnyvale, California, opened the session, stating that current developments in materials for space vehicles could be applied to practical systems for solar energy utilization on the ground. He noted the increasingly major role being played by plastics in the development of solar energy applications, as well as the practical utilization, in present-day space systems, of an electromechanical analogue for the design of a solar heating plant.

According to Gaumer, the fundamental physical theory governing thermal control of spacecraft and practical systems for solar energy utilization are virtually identical, including heat transfer and energy conversion, increase in design efficiency, and improved means of thermal control.

"The task of designing a satellite surface so that it will maintain an average equilibrium temperature of 70°F is remarkably similar to that of designing a solar collecting surface to be used in conjunction with a solar still," said Gaumer. "If a material with the right properties can withstand the rigors of the space environment it should be well suited for use in a terrestrial solar-energy conversion and utilization apparatus.

"The practical demands of the satellite industry have resulted in a very considerable emphasis upon the development of new materials for radioactive thermal control—materials that are stable, reliable, durable and reasonably economical. It seems probable that much of this information will be of equal value to designers of practical terrestrial equipment for solar energy conversion."

Mr. Gaumer further added that aluminum, with the possible addition of beryllium if it can be some day made in thin foil, is indicated as the best surface material for optimum solar collector or concentrator efficiency. Aluminum foil deposited on Mylar or other polyester film could be used to construct an inexpensive solar still, which would fold away like an umbrella and would thus be readily portable and easy to use at all times.

The foregoing illustrations are but a few of the examples one could cite, were space available, of the many ways that rocketry and satellite research and development work and manned space flight are bringing us closer and closer to large-scale utilization of solar energy on earth. It will be a happy sort of irony if in the end man had to travel to the stars in order to make proper use of the sun here at home.

13 POWER FROM FUSION

The most recent discoveries in the field of nuclear physics have helped solve the secret of the sun's power. We have already touched on this in Chapter 6, but we may review briefly here.

All atom nuclei have a positive charge. As always happens with like charges, the nuclei repel each other and resist coming close together. However, because of the immense temperatures prevailing in the interior of the sun—estimated at between 13 and 15 million degrees—particles achieve colossal velocities due to this unimaginable heat. Heavy hydrogen atoms achieve a velocity of 100 miles per second at a temperature of one million degrees C. The velocity increases tenfold when the temperature reaches 100 million degrees. At these tremendous speeds the repulsive force is to some extent overcome and the nuclear particles fuse. This process is called thermonuclear fusion—as opposed to nuclear fission.

It should be noted that only atoms with a low atomic number, and one or two protons in the atom nucleus, can be considered so far as thermonuclear fusion is concerned. When two atomic nuclei of heavy hydrogen fuse at temperatures prevailing in the interior of the sun, the result is an entirely new element, helium 3, which has two protons and a neutron in the nucleus; one neutron is ejected and is converted into energy.

Thermonuclear fusion is achieved in practice by exploding the hydrogen bomb. The "fuse" for such a combustible mixture consisting of light elements is the atom bomb. Until now only the atom bomb has been capable of producing the high temperature needed for thermonuclear fusion.

It is of great importance to find ways of triggering thermonuclear fusion without the use of an atom bomb. In other words, we have to come closer to the process that takes place in the interior of the sun itself.

The difficulties are considerable. They are partly of a technical nature, due to the magnitude of the conversion to be attained, and partly of a fundamental physical nature. The energy necessary to raise the temperature of one gram of heavy hydrogen to 300 million degrees centigrade is 1,000 kilowatts. The charge of a fusion reactor will amount only to a fraction of a gram, but the heat buildup must take place within seconds.

There is a twofold relation between the problem of thermonuclear fusion and the assumptions of theoretical astrophysics. An important contribution to the understanding of how energy is generated in stars was provided by Prof. C. F. von Weizäcker as far back as 1938. The actual difficulties of the task at present do not seem to be connected so much with aspects of nuclear physics as with the fact that properties of ionized gas have to be dealt with under conditions which thus far are beyond present experimental capabilities.

For this reason, the properties of plasma in the presence of magnetic fields have been investigated mainly in connection with astrophysical problems. In certain special and significant cases a solution has been found. The approach is based on the knowledge that nearly all matter in the universe is in a plasma state, and that practically everywhere there are magnetic fields that influence and even determine physical phenomena. Many phenomena in solar physics appear to be dependent on the presence of solar magnetic fields—the shape of sunspots and especially the structure of solar corona. Interplanetary and interstellar space is filled with weak but far-reaching magnetic fields. The study of the interaction between interplanetary and interstellar matter on the one hand and these magnetic fields on the other has become one of the most exciting research tasks in theoretical astrophysics.

Using very simple equipment, Prof. Wilhelm Fuchs and his colleagues of the Institute of Theoretical Physics at the Aachen Institute of Technology succeeded some time ago in producing an electric current of one million amperes in heavy hydrogen plasma lasting one millionth of a second—a practical demonstration for the fusion of heavy hydrogen atom nuclei.

The so-called "pinch effect" is of utmost importance in thermonuclear fusion. Electric currents of extremely high voltage are directed through a gas-filled tube and generate their own magnetic field, forcing the gas from the cooler tube walls to the center and generating temperatures up to 6 million degrees centigrade. By this process, thermonuclear fusion of deuterium atoms (i.e., of the heavy isotope of the hydrogen gas used) takes place, generating a helium isotope and releasing energy. But the generation of energy is not sufficient to obtain an automatic and continuous reaction.

Dr. Lyman Spitzer of Princeton University formulated in 1958 the "stellerator principle." This theory proposes a definite kind of magnetic field that must be produced in order to withdraw and contain the superheated hydrogen gas on the tube wall. The magnetic field is generated by electric currents circulating through coils around the tube. A so-called "rotation transformation" takes place and the gas in the stellerator tube reaches up to approximately one million degrees. The 100 million degrees required for a sustained fusion reaction is to be obtained by a "magnetic pumping process."

Dr. Albert Simon of the Oak Ridge Laboratory of the U.S. Atomic Energy Commission has described the "DCX" method. Deuterium gas particles of very high energy are to be "bombed" into a container where they are retained by magnetic forces. The ions are already heated up to more than 100 million degrees C. The molecules are disintegrated by directing deuterium ions by means of a direct current arc parallel to the magnetic field.

Another process of thermonuclear fusion according to the "mirror principle" has been described by Dr. Richard F. Post of the Livermore Radiation Institute of the University of California. High-energy ions are to be concentrated to a strong magnetic field generated by two large coils. The experiment has been called "mirror principle" because electrically loaded particles are reflected by strong magnetic fields. As soon as the current in the coils is amplified, the hot gas plasma is compressed for a long enough period to reach nuclear fusion.

Large-scale experiments with nuclear fusion have been carried out at the Atomic Energy Research Institute of Harwell, England. In 1958, Harwell surprised the world with the news that generation of temperatures up to 5 million degrees C has been achieved in the research reactor ZETA. Such temperatures could be maintained for one second, but this short time would be sufficient to carry out fusion of heavy hydrogen atoms. The claim to success was withdrawn, however, by Harwell some weeks later.

American scientists succeeded in March 1960 in creating helium by the fusion of hydrogen in fractions of a second, reaching a temperature of 13 million degrees C. The controlled nuclear fusion involved the release of enormous amounts of energy. This process is similar to that which occurs in the interior of the sun. A very old dream of mankind came true: to reach the temperature that prevails in the interior of the sun in order to investigate the greatest secrets of solar physics and astrophysics. By fusion of heavy hydrogen atoms, the process of generating energy which takes place in the sun had been imitated in the laboratory.

The Harwell experts tried to reach the high temperature by sending currents of up to 200,000 amperes through deuterium gas (heavy hydrogen), thus generating an extremely peaceful magnetic field. The gas was compressed in the testing device and heated to such a high temperature that the electrons were stripped off the atom nuclei and the nuclei themselves were fused, thereby releasing neutrons.

The 13-million-degree American experiment mentioned above was carried out by Dr. James L. Tuck and his associates in the Los Alamos Institute, New Mexico; in a magnetic field where hydrogen plasma was compressed in a tube 80-cm long, a fireball was produced consisting of about 50 quadrillions of nuclei of heavy hydrogen per cubic centimeter—at a temperature of about 13 million degrees. Another experiment of thermonuclear fusion was successfully carried out in November, 1960 at the Livermore Laboratory of the University of California. In this case temperatures up to 35 million degrees C were maintained for a fraction of a second. Enormous energies were released in the process.

Soviet scientists like J. Seldovich and A. Sakharov tend to believe that it is possible to dispense with the enormous temperatures in thermonuclear fusion if, instead of electrons, negatively charged *m*-mesons are used. The result would be the formation of *mesoprotons,* which are substantially smaller than atoms. When such an extremely small mesoproton slowly comes closer to an atom of the heavy hydrogen, or deuterium (the deuterium nucleus consisting of one proton and one neutron) then the meson would, theoretically at least, rotate around both of the nuclei which have come close to each other. The *m*-meson acts, so to speak, like a loop-shaped rope around both nuclei. The nuclei will come closer and closer and fuse into one heavy nucleus of helium 3, with a simultaneous release of energy.

The experiments carried out by Professor Alvarez in California are based on the same idea. In a *k*-meson stream Alvarez found *m*-mesons which were "unnecessary" for the experiment and which lasted for only 2 millionths of a second before they disintegrated.

In "flying through," the *m*-meson lost speed and became stationary, acquiring a concentration of energy. According to Alvarez this is what had happened: the negative *m*-meson got into the hydrogen atom and replaced the electron there. The mesoproton, formed as a result, collided with the deuterium (heavy hydrogen) atom and became united with it. The 5.4 million electron volts of energy were transferred to the *m*-meson. After this impulse the *m*-meson became free again and proceeded on its path within the matter until it either collided with another deuterium atom or disintegrated. Thus the possibility of fusing light nuclei at low temperatures had been demonstrated. The utilization of *m*-mesons in thermonuclear fusion for large-scale industrial purposes is not possible because they are so short-lived: they can, as already mentioned, effect a thermonuclear fusion within 2 millionths of a second.

This short detour into low-temperature nuclear fusion shows clearly that thermonuclear fusion at high temperatures has a greater chance of leading to the results so long sought by many a scientist and economist: to have, in about ten years, not only nuclear fission reactors but also thermonuclear fusion reactors—producing energy at half the cost of conventional or fossil fuels.

The fusion experiments to date at temperatures between 5 and 10 million degrees C could not quite duplicate the process occurring in the interior of the sun because the gas of the sun, which produces amounts of nuclear energy sufficient to counteract radiation losses, consists of equal parts of deuterium and tritium, while all the above described experiments were carried out with deuterium alone.

14 THE FUTURE OF SOLAR ENERGY

This chapter is the contribution of Erich A. Farber, Professor of Mechanical Engineering, The University of Florida

It has been pointed out in previous chapters that the fossil fuels which have raised our civilization to the level where it finds itself today are being used up at a tremendous rate. These fuels were put at our disposal by the sun over the ages at an approximate conversion efficiency of 0.3 percent.

For this reason the search for new or thus far neglected sources of energy is being accelerated. Some of the results of these efforts are the development of nuclear energy and the greater emphasis on solar energy.

The present efforts with respect to solar energy can be divided into three groups:

1. A more thorough investigation of the sun as our ultimate source of energy.

2. A study of possible utilization of this energy in outer space.

3. A study of possible utilization of this energy on the surface of the earth.

Under (1) can be cited the efforts of the International Geophysical Year. Despite the great amount of information obtained, much still has to be learned.

In addition to the efforts toward a better understanding of this all-important source of energy, plans are being made for utilizing the energy radiated by the sun for space travel, space stations, and settlements on the moon and other planets. Already the "solar cells" have proved their worth and dependability in space through their performance in satellites. *Vanguard I,* now more than five years in orbit, still generates its electrical needs by direct conversion of the solar radiation.

On the surface of the earth a number of solar-energy laboratories have been set up to further the developments of solar-energy devices that can benefit mankind and raise the living standards all over the world. Three international meetings in 1961—the largest of them the United Nations Conference on New Sources of Energy, with 118 papers on solar energy—emphasized the great need for accelerating the work in this vital and promising field. Many national meetings have endorsed the sentiment of these international gatherings.

Two bills are now before the United States Congress to set up an Office of Solar Energy—an indication of the government's awareness of the importance of and need for this potential source of energy.

THE NATURE AND AVAILABILITY OF SOLAR ENERGY

Efforts are being made to find out more about the characteristics of solar radiation both in outer space and on the surface of the earth. More information is needed. On the surface of the earth there are less than 200 solar-radiation measuring stations and most of them record only the energy falling upon a horizontal surface. Almost half of these stations are located in the United States.

Better information must be obtained, since orientation, local environment, and similar factors can make a tremendous difference.

Less expensive instruments are needed for the collection of solar data.

SOLAR ENERGY COLLECTION AND STORAGE

Solar energy, at the rate of about 1 horsepower per square yard, requires many collectors covering large areas. For this reason their cost per unit area must be low. The roof of an average house provides more than enough area to collect the energy needed within.

The solar energy can be collected as heat with or without concentration for obtaining higher temperatures. Solar energy can also be converted into other forms of energy.

Concentrating collectors need direct, parallel rays of sunlight. They work only on clear days and cannot utilize the diffuse radiation, which in some areas amounts to 50 per cent of the total.

Storage of energy is a general problem, important in many other applications outside the field of solar energy. The most common methods of solar-energy utilization at this time involve heat storage in either water tanks or rock beds, or the use of fusion salts with melting points in the proper range. The salts store the energy by being melted and then give off this stored energy when they recrystallize.

There are cases where storage is not important or inherent in the system. An example is the irrigation by means of solar pumps. They only work during daylight hours, but this is no great disadvantage.

PROPERTIES OF MATERIALS USED IN SOLAR ENERGY WORK

Up to relatively recent times window glass, wood, and metal were the common materials used in solar-energy equipment. Many new and promising materials have been and are being developed. Tinted glass, as well as plastic films with various properties and low cost per unit area, show great promise for solar-energy utilization. Some of these plastic films can be aluminized for reflector use. Recently developed selective surfaces, having high absorptivity and low emissivity, make excellent solar collectors; others with low absorptivity and high emissivity make very effective radiators or sinks.

The materials give to solar-energy devices the ability to be competitive with other systems.

SOLAR ENERGY IN ARCHITECTURE AND AGRICULTURE

The sun has influenced architecture and agriculture for thousands of years. Shelters of various types have been built that take advantage of the natural surroundings—trees, mountains, valleys—

to give just the right solar exposure and resulting comfort. Tinted glass, panels, and the like now give us the opportunity to control the solar effects by other than natural means.

Applications of this type have increased the yield of livestock and poultry. The sun's energy has been used to produce fresh water for cattle, and to heat this water to the proper temperature for drinking.

Through the ages the sun has been the main drying source for agricultural products. Often harvests have been ruined when climatic conditions interfered with this natural phenomenon. Recent experiments have shown that it is economical to spread plastic sheets over large areas and, by blowing air underneath, to increase the rate of drying. This procedure often prevents the spoilage of crops.

SOLAR COOKING AND BAKING

Different designs of solar cookers, utilizing the direct sunshine, and solar ovens with storage capability have been developed.

The technical problems have been solved but it has been found that the social habits of populations, when to cook and how long it should take—facts heretofore ignored—play an extremely important part in increasing the acceptability of the devices. In other words, the time it takes to prepare a meal at the proper hour with solar energy must be about the same as that of the native methods used. Unfortunately the native methods as well as the foods vary greatly all over the world.

SOLAR FURNACES

Solar furnaces have proved their value in research as well as in the industrial production of expensive, high-purity materials. Treatment of materials can be carried out under uncontaminated conditions, in natural air, or in controlled or inert atmospheres when sealed in glass or plastic containers. Very rapid surface heating is possible. Zone refining and the growing of large crystals have made good use of solar furnaces.

Recently the solar furnace has been employed to concentrate light—the shorter wavelengths of the solar spectrum. The rates of chemical reactions have also been increased manifold through application of solar energy.

SOLAR WATER HEATING

Solar water heating is the only commercially available application that has been shown to be competitive with other methods in many parts of the world—including certain parts of the United States, a fuel-rich country. In Japan solar water heaters are being produced at a rate of 100,000 per year. In North Africa and Israel the number of such heaters has increased. In southern Florida the solar water heater is a standard piece of equipment, with about one dozen solar water-heater manufacturers in this state.

A dual-circulation system having a primary circuit with antifreeze solution and a secondary utility water circuit can be used in areas where freezing would damage the conventional type.

Swimming-pool heaters of generally the same design as solar water heaters have become quite popular in the United States, extending the swimming season considerably.

SOLAR HOUSE HEATING

Over one dozen solar houses have been built in various parts of the world. A number of them are not in particularly favorable areas from the point of the amount of solar energy availability. They use hot water and hot air as the transport media, and water, rock bin or fusion salt for heat storage. All these houses have proved the technical feasibility of solar house heating, but they have also shown that these systems, at least when custom-built and backed up by a conventional system, are too expensive to install at this time.

In southern locations where simple solar heaters can be used to take the chill out of the house in the morning, the picture is more favorable.

SOLAR COOLING AND REFRIGERATION

It is believed by many experienced people in the field that solar refrigeration and cooling is, next to solar water heating, the most promising application of solar energy. When cooling is needed most, the energy available to do the job is greatest. Also inherent in the absorption system, which is the system most widely used, storage is no problem since the refrigerant can be kept in a tank indefinitely until needed.

Last but not least, it has been pointed out that cooling and refrigeration for food preservation is one of the greatest needs in the world today, and that if spoilage could be prevented many of the famines in the world today would not occur.

Older systems used concentrating devices to produce high-temperature heat. Within the last few years, low-temperature systems such as the three-ton system at the University of Florida Solar Energy Laboratory, utilizing inexpensive flatplate collectors, have been designed and tested. These systems have the advantage that they utilize both direct and diffuse radiation and will therefore also operate on cloudy days. The flat-plate collectors provide hot water from 120°F to about 200°F as heat source.

SOLAR POWER, ENGINES AND PUMPS

A number of engines and pumps have been described previously. Some of these have been developed before the advent of gasoline engines. Rather large power plants up to 100 horsepower were built around the turn of the century.

Within the last few years the small steam engine (operating from the steam generated by a concentrating solar collector), and hot-air engines of different designs—especially small, high-speed steam turbines—have appeared and show great promise. Dr. Tabor in Israel has demonstrated a 5-horsepower solar plant using a high molecular weight vapor turbine.

Some rather large solar power plants have been designed and planned for space-station use.

SOLAR EVAPORATION AND DISTILLATION

The production of fresh water (one of the costliest commodities to those who do not have it, yet taken for granted by those who do) from brackish or salt water is being studied extensively. The first large solar still, built in 1883, covered 4,800 square feet and delivered 23 tons of fresh water per day. Since then, small units have been investigated by the various solar laboratories and the Office of Saline Water of the United States Department of the Interior. The new materials mentioned earlier show promise of allowing the construction of inexpensive stills competitive with other methods. At this time many improvements have been made in efficiency and performance, but only at an increase in cost.

If the solar stills are so constructed as to collect rain water at the same time, their yield can in many areas be greatly increased— doubled or even tripled. The combining of a still with other devices such as engines and condensing the exhaust vapor from the engines to fresh water is under consideration.

SOLAR CONVERTERS

(a) *Photovoltaic*. By far the greatest amount of money spent thus far on solar energy has been in the development of direct conversion techniques. One of the results of this effort, the silicon cell, has proved its value in space applications but at this time is too expensive for general use. Cells of this type with conversion efficiencies of 15 percent have been made. Their theoretical limit is 22 percent, since they utilize only the short-wavelength portion of the solar spectrum. Other cells are being developed with extended band span. It has been found that if the cells are kept cool, their output is many times that at higher temperature.

For outer space applications, high-energy, radiation-resistant cells have been developed.

Polycrystaline films, which are much less expensive and thus can be used over large areas, are now under development.

(b) *Thermoelectric*. Generators of this type are often referred to as "superthermocouples" and produce electric current from a difference in temperature. Most of those used today are alloys of tellurium and give conversion efficiencies of about 8 percent. A pilot plant of 170 square feet is in operation near Toulon, France. It utilizes 4 × 4-inch bi-telluride couples covered with selective aluminum and two glass plates. Based upon the performance of this unit, a 900 square foot system is contemplated.

In Japan, powder metallurgy has been employed to reduce the cost of these units.

(c) *Thermionic*. Converters of this type (thermocells) have a hot cathode (up to 4800°F) giving off electrons and a cold collector anode. The high temperatures are produced through concentration in a solar furnace or with a Fresnal lens or mirror. Conversion efficiencies of up to 13 percent have been obtained in 12- to 15-watt/cm^2 units.

PHOTOCHEMISTRY AND PHOTOSYNTHESIS

Much progress has been made in the understanding of the way in which the sun, together with chemical processes and the mechanism of living organisms, produces our food and fuels. Much still needs to be learned.

Algae have been put to work experimentally to produce at an accelerated rate in a closed system, the basic nutritional needs to sustain life.

A recent promising analogy between the photosynthetic process and that of semiconductors has been reported. If this theory is correct it should be possible, before too long, to duplicate some of the processes of nature.

SOLAR PONDS

Solar ponds are large bodies of water, natural or man-made, from 3 to 10 feet deep, with radiation-absorbing layers near the bottom. These ponds absorb the solar radiation and are heated to reasonably high temperatures near the bottom. By "doping" these ponds with salts, the hot layers stay near the bottom, and conventional heat engines can be operated between the hot bottom and cool upper layers. These ponds are inexpensive and may cover large areas. More work needs to be done with these ponds, but at this time they show great promise.

It might be well to mention again that one of the greatest needs today is the utilization of solar energy for food preservation. This is especially true on the Asiatic and African continents.

New materials are constantly being developed for this important application. Glasses with various coatings have been produced for specific solar applications. Plastics with low absorptivity and reflectivity, improved wind-flexing properties, wettability, and heat resistance, combined with selective surfaces, show great promise as materials for the future.

Satisfactory energy storage, a problem not unique to solar applications, is, however, badly needed.

Solar cells will provide the power for low energy requirements in space. For larger capacity, more or less conventional designs will be needed. The *Sunflower I* project, a solar power system for space stations, employs a 45-foot reflector that provides the heat for a three-stage turbine operating at 24,000 rpm. This system uses rubidium as the working fluid, sodium fluoride as the high-temperature (1875°F) storage medium, and lithium hydride for low-temperature (1250°F) storage. This unit is designed to give a conversion efficiency of 26.5 percent.

At the present time most of the work in the field of solar energy is being done by the industrialized countries who have the know-how and the money; unfortunately these countries do not have a great need for the practical applications. The countries that need the end product of such investigations, and would use them economically and competitively, are the so-called underdeveloped countries, which unfortunately do not have the know-how or the money for this work.

Even though terrestrial applications of solar energy are not supported as much as they should be, while most of the money is spent on space applications, many of the results obtained from these latter efforts will eventually find use on the earth's surface.

FACTS AND FIGURES ABOUT THE SUN

Distance of sun from earth
  based on solar parallax of 8″.80 .... 92,913,000 *miles*

Solar parallax (angle of earth's disk
as seen from sun), according to:

Aristarchos of Samos (260 B.C.) .... 3′
Ptolemy (Claudius Ptolemaeus, A.D. 130) ..... 2′
Johannes Kepler .... 1′ ("not over")
Jacques Cassini (1672) .... 9″.50
Johann Encke (1824) .... 8″.57
Powalky and Stone (1870) .... 8″.79 − 8″.91
Sir David Gill (1877) .... 8″.75
Arthur Auwers (1882) .... 8″.75 − 8″.88
Simon Newcomb (1895) .... 8″.797
Henry N. Russell (1926) .... 8″.802 ± 0″.004
Magnus Nyren (1935) .... 8″.81
Sir Harold Spencer Jones (1941) .... 8″.790 ± 0″.001
Adopted by science .... 8″.799 ± 0″.004

Difference in distance of sun from earth
  between January and June .... 3,069,000 *miles*

Diameter of the solar system (orbit of Pluto) .. 7,440,000,000 *miles*

Distance to nearest star (Proxima Centauri) .... 4.15 *light years*
                                             25,000,000,000,000 *miles*

Diameter of Milky Way galaxy .... 50,000–200,000 *light years*

Angular diameter of sun .... 31'59".3
Linear diameter of sun .... 864,000 *miles*
Ratio of sun's diameter to earth's 109.3:1

Volume of sun compared to earth 1,300,000:1
Mass of sun compared to earth 332,488:1

Average density of sun (compared to water) 1.41:1

Surface gravity of sun compared to earth's 28.0:1

Solar constant (average amount of radiation
from sun in calories per square centimeter
per minute), according to:
Pouillet 1.76
Forbes 2.72
Crova 2.32
Violle 2.54
Adopted by science .... 1.94 *cal/cm²/min*
429 *Btu/sq ft/hr*
.354 *watts/sq meter/sec*
.36 × 10⁶ *ergs/cm²/sec*

Surface area of sun, compared with earth's 11,940:1

Weight of sun .... 2,000 quadrillion *tons*
As percentage of mass of entire solar system .... 97.7 *percent*

Energy reserve of the sun .... 1.785 × 10⁵⁴ *ergs*

Energy released by sun in one year .... 1.2 × 10⁴¹ *ergs*

Luminosity (amount of heat and light
radiated per square centimeter per
second) according to Stefan-Boltzmann
law .... 1,490 *cal/sec*

Luminous energy of sun, absolute .... 525 × 10²¹ *horsepower*
92.4 × 10²⁴ *calories*

Total radiation of sun .... 3.86 × 10³³ *ergs/sec*
Amount received by earth .... 3.78 × 10²³ *ergs/sec*
85 trillion *kilowatts*

Portion received by outer atmosphere of earth
(less than billionth of total) .... 170 trillion *kilowatts*
Solar energy received in United States
annually .... 9,000 trillion *kilowatt-hours*
Equivalent to .... 1,150 billion *tons of coal*

Thickness of chromosphere .... up to 10,000 *miles*
Mass of chromosphere (Eddington) .... 120,000,000 *tons*

Age of sun, according to
Kelvin (1890) .... 20 million *years*
Savage (1960) .... over 24 billion *years*
Hoyle (1960) .... over 15 billion *years*

```
Bonnor (1960) ................... "cycles of 10 billion years"
Eddington (1930) ....................... 5,200 trillion years
Radioactive dating ........................ 5 billion years
```

Time for one complete solar rotation
```
    At equator ................................. 25 earth days
    At poles ................................... 37 earth days
```

Angle of solar axis to plane of earth's orbit .... 7°15′

Orbital velocity of earth around sun .... 18.5 miles/sec

Speed of light (Mt. Wilson Observatory, 1931) ... 186,284 miles/sec

Light year .... 5,880,000,000,000 miles

Surface temperature of sun, degrees centigrade,
    according to
```
    Pouillet .................................... 1,461–1,761
    Secchi ........................... 7,156,800–1,000,000,000
    Ericsson ........................................ 4,000
    Kelvin ..................................... 3,000–6,000
    Violle .......................................... 1,500
    Zöllner ........................................ 28,000
    Gray ........................................... 8,000
    Wilson ......................................... 8,000
    Stefan ......................................... 6,500
    Wien ........................................... 5,880
    Adopted by science ............................. 6,000
```

Interior temperature of sun, degrees centigrade,
    according to
```
    Eddington .................................. 30,000,000
    Gamow ...................................... 20,000,000
    Krogdahl ................................... 14,000,000
```

Temperature range from chromosphere to corona, based
    on measurements made 1959–61 by R. Grant Athay and
    others at University of Colorado High Altitude
    Observatory, Boulder, Colo. ...."jumps" from 10,000,
                                        50,000 and 1,000,000° C

Loss of solar mass due to radiation .. 4,200,000 ton/sec⎫ of hydrogen
                    140,000,000,000,000 tons/year⎭ to helium

Wavelengths in electromagnetic spectrum
    (1 angstrom unit = .0001 micron)
```
        cosmic rays and gamma rays   less than 0.01–1.5    angstrom units
        X-ray radiation .................... 10–1000
        Ultraviolet radiation ................ 25–4000  (= .4 micron)
        Visible light
            violet ...................... 3600–4300
            indigo ...................... 4300–4550
            blue ........................ 4550–4920
            green ....................... 4920–5500
```

```
yellow ....................... 5500–5880
orange ....................... 5885–6470
red .......................... 6470–8000  (= .8 micron)
Infrared radiation ................ 8000–0.04   cm
Electric sparks .................. 0.01–10     cm
Radio waves ...................... 1–10,000 cm
```

Amospheric pressure at high altitudes, pounds per square inch

```
20,000  feet ............................... 5.12
60,000   "   ............................... 1.53
90,000   "   ............................... 0.119
    40 miles ............................... 0.00046
   100   "   ............................... 0.00000083
   285   "   ............................... 0.00000000067
```

INDEX

thermocouples, 107–110, 160
thermonuclear reactions, 18–19, 36–42, 149–153
Thompson Ramo Wooldridge, Inc., 111
Thomson, William, Lord Kelvin, 28
Threlkeld, J. L., 6
tidal energy, 11
transistor, 100
Trombe, Félix, 33, 86–90
Tschirnhaus, Walter von, 44
Tuck, James L., 152
TVA, 2

W

water power, 11
Weizsäcker, Carl von, 38, 150
Whillier, Austin, 61
Wien, Wilhelm, 28
Wien's law, 82
Wildt, P., 26
Willsie, E. E., 48
Wilson, A., 20
Wilson, C. T. R., 28
Wilson, Volney C., 109
Witsch, H. von, 122
Wolff, Michael F., 110 n.
Wollaston, William Hyde, 26

U

ultraviolet radiation, 124–132
United Nations conference, 68
University of Florida, 159

Y

Young, Charles Augustus, 23–24, 31

V

Van Allen belts, 135, 144
Vanguard I, 103, 135, 145, 155
Violle, Jules, 28, 32
Vitense, E., 26

Z

ZETA reactor, 152
Ziegler, Hans, 145
Ziem, Theodore, 54
Ziolkovsky, Konstantin, 133
Zollner, Johann Karl, 23, 28